Balancing the Scales
A Faith-Based Study Guide and Fitness Plan for Life

RON HENDERSON

 GLADROCK PUBLISHING

P.O. Box 483
Anoka, MN 55303

DEDICATION

This book is dedicated to the late Jack Lalanne, who taught me through his early morning television shows, the importance of healthy eating and exercise, and who wasn't afraid to give honor to God publicly; and to the numerous pastors who have entrusted me over the years with their health and their lives.

CONTENTS

ACKNOWLEDGMENTS

The Holy Spirit for leading and guiding me through the writing of this book, and my Father in heaven who has poured out His grace and love on me amidst my short comings and imperfections.

My wife, who has been my biggest supporter and helpmate, and for her endless hours spent editing this book.

My many clients and friends that have allowed me into their lives through physical training and prayer.

My father, Russell Henderson, and my dear mother, Rachel Lyga, for the examples they set about the importance of physical health and balance.

RON HENDERSON

FOREWORD

If you're fortunate in this Christian life you may come across an individual who seems to have scripture so ingrained in their heart and mind that they really are a living testimony of grace, redemption, and faithfulness. That is Ron Henderson. As his wife, I can attest to his patience and dedication. No matter what happens in day-to-day life, he turns to the Word of God for direction, wisdom, and comfort. His internal compass points to Christ. He will be the first to admit that he is not perfect. He is quick to say 'I'm sorry' and quick to forgive. Most of all, he has a heart to help others.

Ron truly cares about people and desires to see them healthy—both spiritually and physically. His heart breaks when he sees people who are short-changing themselves out of joy, vigor, and years by neglecting their physical health and fitness. This is especially true when he sees people approaching their later years with limited strength and mobility. It is this passion that pushed him on to complete *Balancing the Scales: A Faith-Based Study Guide and Fitness Plan for Life.* He desires to see God's people living at their best. I pray you read this book with an open heart and allow the scriptures and information within to bear good fruit in your life.

RON HENDERSON

PREFACE

I wrote the book, *Fitness and Faith: Balancing the Scales,* several years ago, from a desire to help individuals understand the connection between fitness and faith. Soon after the book was published, I received numerous requests to develop the book into a group study guide. People wanted to go through the material in a small group setting, similar to a bible study, so they could share their journey with others who want to improve their health and faith. I was excited to rise to the challenge and *Balancing the Scales: A Faith-Based Study Guide and Fitness Plan for Life* was born. I have added additional material to the original book, including group study questions, individual reflection points, and opportunities to put your desires and plans into action. As you embark on this journey, whether studying individually or in a group setting, I pray you not only increase in health, but in faith, as well. *Balancing the Scales* is not a get-fit-quick guide, but a faith-based guide for LIFE!

RON HENDERSON

INTRODUCTION

To understand the connection between fitness and faith, one must understand that there is no complete fitness without real faith. I have been a top personal trainer for over three decades, and even I was unable to achieve my top fitness physically until I started on my journey to become spiritually fit. You may not be a personal trainer or in the fitness industry but perhaps you will see some aspects of your own life in my story.

My childhood years were fairly normal. My parents took me to church almost every Sunday, but I had never really heard the plan of salvation until I was eighteen years old. I remember being at church summer camp and my youth pastor, Paul Fosmark, was singing, *"I surrender all, I surrender all, all to Jesus I surrender, I surrender all..."* I remember how hard it was for me to sing that song because I knew in my heart, I hadn't given my all to Jesus.

You see, I had not made Jesus my personal Savior. In fact, there had never been a time in my life that I lived for God until that day. It was then that I accepted Jesus as my Savior and started to live for Him. Even after that commitment, I found myself falling away from God after a few years and was constantly backsliding. It seemed that no matter how much I tried I could never keep a consistent walk with God. I wanted to in my heart, but my flesh was weak. Jesus said "Watch and pray so that you will not fall into temptation. The spirit is willing but the flesh is weak" (Matthew 26:41).

That was me trying to live for God through my own power. I was constantly struggling because I still had not surrendered my all. Like so many people who have tried diet

after diet only to fail, I was running to this pastor and that pastor and from church to church. I had no victory. I spent many nights crying for the peace of God, but there was no peace.

As I look back at those early years of my Christian life it is evident that I never really crucified my flesh. I did everything else except rein in my fleshly desires. I meant well but that is not enough. Jesus wants our all: our mind, our body, and our spirit. It wasn't until November 2003 that I made a true commitment to the things of God. It was then that I received deliverance from my fleshly ways. I made a permanent decision to give it all to Jesus and in return Jesus gave me His all. Jesus is so real to me that when I speak to people about my transformation the tears start to flow down my face. His peace is so real to me now; but that peace did not come to me until I made a decision to surrender my all.

If you are tired of bouncing from diet to diet and from prayer line to prayer line you will have to give it all to Jesus in every area of your life. If that means eating less, then you will have to eat less. If it means changing your diet, then you will have to change it. Get resolute and ask Jesus to help you make the changes that you desire. If you are reading this book, then you have some areas in your life that you need to completely turn over to Jesus. If you do this then Jesus will help you get what he has promised to you—life, and that abundantly (John 10:10). You have a right to be in good shape, to have more energy, and to feel good. Don't let the devil steal what is rightly yours.

I pray that you will not live another day as a defeated Christian either in the physical or spiritual areas of your life. Jesus is there knocking. I pray you let Him in.

CHAPTER ONE

BALANCING THE SCALES

"Iron sharpens iron; so one man sharpens another."
Proverbs 27:17

Fitness and Faith: A Great Mix

When you think about it, most Christians or people of faith prepare for life on earth and life in heaven by striving for godliness of heart and behavior. Although we can't determine how long we or our family members will live, we do have some power over the quality of our family's physical and spiritual lives to some extent. By raising children in a godly household they have every opportunity to accept Jesus Christ as their Lord and Savior. Some of us prepare financially by saving money for ourselves and our children's future. But what about our health and the health of our children? Are we setting good examples for them to follow? If not, then this is a perfect time to start because our physical and spiritual health are the most important things in this life.

The apostle Paul reminds us in 2 Corinthians 5:17 that, "...if any man be in Christ, he is a new creature: old things are passed away; behold all things are become new."

1

The old person you were before you encountered the saving grace of Jesus Christ could not make the changes necessary; but, the new you can! With God *all* things are possible. I'm not saying that you will be free from every challenge immediately, because I don't know what you are struggling with or what your circumstances are. What I do know is that if you release it all to the Lord you will begin to see a change in your heart, mind, and behavior. For some, these changes might happen immediately. For others, it may take longer. As the old adage states, "I am not sinless, but I sin less."

Like many Christians who bounce from diet to diet, or from workout plan to workout plan, or from smoking to not smoking and back to smoking. If we want to walk in good health and gain freedom in those troubling areas, we will have to give it all to Jesus in both the physical and spiritual areas of our lives. Once we make the decision to give our struggles to the Lord, He does not leave us helpless. He lifts our burdens and gives us the strength to live in a manner that pleases Him in every area of life. When we give our heart to God, living for Him no longer becomes an impossible and frustrating chore but a joyful journey.

One Big Lie

One of the many lies straight from the devil is to convince you that people who work out are too concerned about the flesh, or that they are vain because they're focusing on themselves and not on God. The truth is that people who exercise and are thoughtful about taking care of their bodies are really glorifying God. Remember, the devil is sly and treacherous and will do anything he can to keep you from strengthening your body as well as your mind. People who are in shape spiritually, physically, and mentally are a huge threat to the kingdom of darkness. The devil wants to keep us with no energy, sick, weak, and frustrated so we will be ineffective in our lives and in sharing God's good news and love to the world. No matter where you are in your spiritual walk, you need to know that taking care of your body is actually a requirement.

New Year's Resolutions

According to surveys, three of the top ten New Year's resolutions made by Americans are health and fitness related. The number one resolution is to lose weight. I would guess that most people have that resolution on the top of their list year after year. Losing weight is a struggle for so many folks in this fast food and sedentary culture. I am here to tell you that losing weight is achievable without going to extremes with crazy diets and insane workout programs. How do we do this? We can start by obeying one of the greatest commandments: *love our neighbor as ourselves.* But do we love ourselves? Do we love ourselves enough to take care of what the Lord has given us? Before we can love others we have to be able to love who we are! God says that you are fearfully and wonderfully made (Psalm 139:14). You can believe it because God said it and He does not lie (Numbers 23:19).

To help others we must not only love ourselves but also have some stamina. Have you ever been really sick or tired and someone tried to talk to you? Although you wanted to be there for them in spirit your body wasn't able. When you are not feeling your best it is hard to be attentive to other people's needs no matter how much you want to. That is why it is so important that we all start to see that our body is really on loan from God.

Our body houses the Spirit of the Living God. It is truly not our own for we are bought with a price (1Corinthians 6:9); therefore, we ought to glorify God in body, mind, and spirit. We can pray and ask Jesus to help us love our neighbor as ourselves and He will. We can even read the bible more and memorize verse after verse. All these things will help us become a better person spiritually speaking, but these things will do very little to help us reshape ourselves physically, unless we apply physical action to our situation. We are living in a physical world and therefore it will take some physical action to make the changes that most of us desire. As we apply these actions for the right reasons all the other things we are seeking will follow. "But seek ye first the kingdom of God, and his righteousness; and all these things shall be added unto you." (Matthew 6:33). These things' can be more energy, feeling better, looking better, and living longer.

Have you ever seen that tired, 'no-time-for-you' look in pastors? Well, I have! They are so exhausted from the demands on their time and the needs of people that you ask them a question and they look at you like, "Please hurry up. I'm tired." You wonder if they are even hearing you through their weariness. Unfortunately, this is all too common. First of all, we live in a society where we find ourselves so busy that we barely have time to eat right, let alone exercise or listen to someone else's problem. The demands on people in ministry are even more exhausting. There are times they simply must push on even if they have nothing left to give.

This is why a fitness routine is so important. It gives us the extra fuel we need. Exercise actually generates energy! Now, I know the Holy Ghost can give you power when you are ministering or any time, for that matter. But if we were more adamant about taking better care of our health we would have even more energy to do whatever God has planned for us. If we don't keep our bodies in shape, we will be missing out on all of what God has in store for us. Remember, God wants *all* of us and respecting what He has

4

given us glorifies Him. The Scriptures say to do all to the glory of God, so let's start moving and glorifying Him. If you keep making the same New Year's resolutions year after year, maybe you should look at the motivation behind your decisions, and then make your resolutions with the sole purpose of honoring God.

TIME FOR ACTION

Fitness and Faith

Fitness and faith—that is a great mix! God wants to be involved in every aspect of our lives. He wants us to be healthy, not only for our benefit, but for the benefit of others. We need to have strength, stamina, and vitality as we accomplish what God has planned for our mission in life. If you're tired you can't present yourself at your best. If you are out of shape you may not be able to live out your years with vitality, or, you may not have as many years as you would have, had you taken care of your body. Balancing the scales is about living life to the fullest and with moderation. This might sound contradictory, but you cannot have life at its fullest if you are over-indulging in things that are not helpful or healthful. Even over-indulging in good things can cause problems!

Start with Reflecting

With God *all* things are possible! That doesn't mean we won't have challenges, but God is able to walk with you through your challenges and see you come out on the other side victoriously. The following questions will help you to reflect on where you are in your fitness and faith journey:

1. What is your purpose for working through *Balancing the Scales* at this time in your life?

   _____
   _____
   _____
   _____
   _____

2. What health and/or weight loss challenges are you facing?

   _____
   _____
   _____
   _____
   _____

3. Are any of those challenges more difficult than the others? Do they make obtaining your goals exceptionally difficult?

   _____
   _____
   _____
   _____
   _____

4. What items identified in the above question have you struggled to surrender to the Lord?

   _____
   _____
   _____
   _____
   _____

5. Take the opportunity to surrender those areas listed

above to the Lord and ask Him for help overcoming the temptation to return to old patterns.

6. Review the Power Verses at the end of this chapter and choose one or two to memorize. Repeat the verses until they resonate in your spirit and effect change. Whenever a temptation arises, or you are faced with one of the challenges you identified, repeat the Power Verse until you feel the chains being broken. Make this a practice in your life; apply it to all types of circumstances and see the power of the scriptures at work in your life.

    a. Power Verse 1: _____

    b. Power Verse 2: _____

Resolutions

Many Americans have health or fitness goals as one of their top New Year's Resolutions but often give up after a few weeks. Health and fitness is more than a goal or resolution. Being healthy and fit comes from a lifestyle of healthy choices. The following questions will help you take inventory of what you have done that has worked for you, and what has not worked.

1. What types of eating programs (diets) have you tried in your quest to lose or to gain weight?

    _____
    _____
    _____
    _____
    _____
    _____

2. What eating program(s) have worked best for you and why?

_____

_____

_____

_____

_____

3. What eating programs did *not* work for you and why?

_____

_____

_____

_____

4. What is the difference between a *diet* and a *lifestyle*?

_____

_____

_____

_____

_____

5. Read Matthew 6:33. What do you want to add to yourself physically?

_____

_____

_____

_____

What do you want to add to yourself spiritually?

_____

_____

_____

_____

_____

6. Is there something God has planned for you to be or do that being physically unfit or having lack of energy is preventing you from accomplishing?

_____

_____

_____

_____

_____

_____

_____

_____

_____

Being health conscious and taking care of your body is not vanity, it's good stewardship of the gift God has given you. It is glorifying to God. It is not only prudent to take care of yourself; it is your responsibility.

POWER VERSES

Iron sharpens iron, so one man sharpens another.
Proverbs 27:17

Therefore if anyone is in Christ, he is a new creature; the old things are passed away; behold, new things have come.
2 Corinthians 5:17

I will give thanks to You, for I am fearfully and wonderfully made; wonderful are Your works, and my soul knows it very well. Psalm 139:14

For you have been bought with a price: therefore glorify God in your body. 1 Corinthians 6:20

God is not a man, that he should lie, nor a son of man, that he should repent; Has He said, and will He not do it? Or has He spoken, and will He not make it good?
Numbers 23:19

But seek first His kingdom and His righteousness, and all these things will be added to you. Matthew 6:33

CHAPTER TWO

BLESSED AND EQUIPPED

In all these things we are more than conquerors
through him that loved us.
Romans 8:37

You Need a Revelation

About 20 years ago, I received a revelation in the area of sickness. I used to always get sick. If a co-worker got a cold, I knew I would get it. If my best friend got the flu, I just knew I would come down with it and I usually did. If I woke up in the morning with a dry throat and sneezing, I would immediately say, "I think I am coming down with something." Later that day—low and behold—I did indeed come down with something. My mind and my words were working against me, not for me. Proverbs 18:21 states, "Death and life are in the power of the tongue, and those who love it will eat its fruit." This basically means that we can get ourselves into all sorts of trouble with our mouths. We can speak out something and our minds believe it.

I was definitely manifesting what I was declaring. When I finally got tired of being sick all the time, I made a conscious decision to change the way I talked. The more I spoke the positive, the fewer times I would actually get sick. I kept practicing the positive approach—which is biblical—and now, 30 years later, I can't remember the last time I was actually sick. The reason I'm telling you this is that it's extremely important that you stop telling yourself the negative. I'm here to tell you that you CAN lose weight. You CAN eat healthy. You CAN walk up those stairs instead of taking the elevator. You CAN start fitness training. You CAN stick to a healthy lifestyle. You CAN finally accomplish that number one New Year's resolution.

Diets, for the most part, don't work. What does work is consistency in the way you exercise, moderation in the way you eat, and positive thoughts spoken to yourself and to others. Most people have heard of the placebo effect, which is based on the theory that you believe a pill or something you are taking will benefit you. You *believe* that the prescription will make you feel better and heal your sickness. What happens is that your *belief* causes your body to respond. For years I have preached to people the importance of engaging your mind in everything you do.

I don't allow myself to get sick. I do that by not letting a cough turn into a cold. For example, maybe you wake up and your nose is a little congested. You may say to yourself, 'I hope I am not getting a cold.' Well, my friend, the moment you even admit that maybe you're getting a cold the more likely you are to manifest the symptoms. The fact may be that you have rolled over in your sleep and that caused your nose to be plugged up or that the fan you had blowing on you dried out your mucus membranes. I know that every time I get a massage, if I am lying on my stomach for more than ten minutes, when I get up I am stuffy. If I didn't know what I know, I would think, 'I must be coming down with a cold.' I use my mind by choosing not to receive anything negative. If

12

everyone in your office has come down with the stomach flu and you notice that your stomach is a little upset after eating lunch, don't think that you might have the flu. Instead, recognize the fact that maybe something you ate is adversely affecting your stomach.

Now, every situation is different. How you respond has to be based on your particular situation. I would be the first person to tell you that if you know you are truly sick, seek medical help. But don't *look* for illness in a sniffle or stomachache. As I said earlier, I have not been sick in over 30 years. You can control a lot of what happens to you. Obviously, if you have any serious health issues always check with your doctor before embarking on any fitness or eating plan.

Take Inventory

People's opinion of themselves varies greatly depending on their life experiences, mental fortitude, and emotional make up. I think I can safely say that everybody has things they like about their body and things they do not like that they wish they could change. The things we cannot change need to be accepted as our unique God-ordained design. The famous actress and singer, Ethel Waters, coined the phrase, "God doesn't make junk." My stepdaughter was born with a physical disability to the degree that she has never been able to walk or even move her legs. I could say she is 'confined' to a wheelchair, or that she is 'wheelchair bound,' but that would be looking at her situation in a limiting light. This young lady 'gets around' by wheelchair. She goes to work and even had her own apartment. "God doesn't make junk" and He certainly doesn't make mistakes. Do not waste any time bemoaning what you cannot change.

Are there aspects of your body you don't like and *can*

change? That is where you can concentrate your efforts. How important is it for you to tone your abdomen or build those muscles in your arms and legs? How would you feel if you could reach some of your fitness and stamina goals? What have you been neglecting to do to reach a greater level of fitness? Answering these questions may be convicting for you. It is amazing how much of what we don't like about ourselves are within our power to change—that is our choices, our habits, and our mindfulness. The biggest choice is to rely on the help of the Holy Spirit who gives us the strength to do what we have tried and failed to do on our own (John 14:26). Paul writes to the Philippian church, "I can do all things through Him who strengthens me" (Philippians 4:13). As Christians, we have a Helper who is ready to give us strength when we need it. That is something Jenny Craig can't do. Weight Watchers is not going to stand by your side late at night whispering "don't do it" as you are staring at the Hagen Das ice cream in the freezer. These programs may be helpful for you and, if this is the case, I say go for it!

But the fact remains, to overcome the bondages and struggles that we face we must rely on the power of God. He is the author of freedom! Christians have an advantage in overcoming. Let's take advantage of our advantage! Romans 8:37 states, "...in all these things we are more than conquerors through Him who loved us."

The reality is, we can pray all day long. We can even fast, but we cannot expect God to perform a miracle if we don't take the right steps ourselves. God gives us a choice and we just need to get off of the couch. I believe God wants us to do our part. God expects us to move our body, to exercise if we physically can, and to take care of ourselves. Jesus told a story as recorded in Matthew 25:14-30. It is the parable of the talents. The story, in brief, recounts a man going on a journey and giving three of his servants each a sum of money (talents) according to each of his ability. One received five, another received two, and a third received one. The first one invested his five talents and doubled his investment. The second servant invested and doubled his money as well. The third one was afraid of losing the one talent his master gave him, so he buried it in the ground. When the master returned he was pleased with the first two but angry with the one who buried his money stating, "You wicked and slothful servant! You knew that I reap where I have not sown and gather where I scattered no seed. Then you ought to have invested my money with the bankers, and at my coming I should have received what was my own with interest. So take the talent from him and give it to him who has the ten talents" (vs. 26-28).

Everything we have comes from God and belongs to Him. Each of us has been entrusted with resources of time and materials. We are responsible for using those resources so that they increase in value. As Christians, we also have the Word of God. If we believe, understand, and then apply His Word as good stewards we will be a blessing to others and the value of what we do will be multiplied. Remember, we are accountable to the Lord for what He has bestowed upon us "to each according to his ability"(v.15).

One of the Biggest Mistakes

One of the biggest mistakes we can make when we're starting an exercise program is to be too hard on ourselves. What I mean by that is that we expect too much from ourselves too early in our training regimen. If we miss a workout we feel guilty. If we eat something we know we shouldn't have eaten we feel condemned. My friend, let me tell you that you should not feel condemned. It will take time and work to get to where you want to be. Remember that to grow spiritually it takes reading the Word, praying, and worshiping God. When you learned a new task it took practice and perseverance. Everything you do takes time. It took time to gain weight and it will take time to take it off. Our physical bodies can be like our spiritual bodies in some regards, for there are many layers that will need peeling in order for us to get to where we need to be. This peeling can take months if not years in some cases. If we continue our spiritual and health journey and don't give up we will receive all of the blessing of God in the spiritual and physical.

The devil would like you to give up and he'll even say things to you like, "You might as well stop exercising since you missed a week," or, "Why pray today since you didn't pray yesterday?". He lies to get you frustrated and discouraged. Don't listen when you hear that voice speaking to you. If it is not the voice of God speaking to you cover your ears, for listening will only hinder you from reaching your goals. All things worth having are worth working for, so slow down and keep your eyes on the prize and finish your course. The better physical shape you are in the more alert you tend to be.

The bible teaches that we should be sober and vigilant "...because your adversary the devil, as a roaring lion, walketh about, seeking whom he may devour." (1 Peter 5:8). When I was in boot camp we each had to take our turns at night on what they called 'fire watch,' which was really security for the barracks. While on watch, one thing we all found out quickly was how important it was to be well rested. If you were tired it would be much easier for someone to sneak up on you.

It is the same in our Christian walk. If we are physically out of shape we leave a little space for the devil to sneak into our lives. We may lose our tempers and say things we know

16

we shouldn't say or listen to things we know we shouldn't listen to. Have you ever had someone tell you a juicy tidbit of information you knew was gossip, but because you were tired you listened anyway and allowed that negative energy into your mind? You most likely have. Be on guard and resist the tricks of the enemy of your faith. Pray that God would open your ears so you can hear what the Spirit is saying regarding your spiritual and physical well-being.

Sin or Slip

If we want to have victory in our lives it is important that when we sin, we confess it immediately. The longer we wait to confess our sin the more we distance ourselves from God and the harder it is to come back. This is exactly what the devil wants. As long as we live in these bodies of flesh we will sin, but we can have the victory.

When you start exercising and eating healthy don't be discouraged or stop training just because you missed a scheduled workout or ate something you knew you shouldn't have eaten. That slip does not have to be the end of your perseverance. It's common for a lot of people to not want to continue because they are frustrated and feel defeated. That is exactly where the devil wants you—moping around with no energy and no physical power.

I'm here to tell you that you have spiritual power if you are living for God. If you're not in shape and are overweight, you may be somewhat defeated in the physical realm and not even know it. That is why it is so important, if you miss a workout or have a bad food day, that you forgive yourself and get right back into your workout and eating plan. Every day that you walk with God is a victorious day and every day that you stick with your workout plan is a day of victory. All those other days, if you have confessed them, are forgiven and

17

behind you. God wants us to prosper in all areas of our life: spiritually, physically, personally, and financially. Isn't it time we called on Jesus—the One who gave us life—and ask Him for His guidance and help? Say this prayer with me right now:

> *Jesus, I need help in getting my body in shape. I need help in controlling my appetite. I need help in controlling my tongue. Lord, help me to resist what I need to resist and to do what I know I should do. I rebuke all those thoughts that the devil would put before me and I draw near to Your thoughts and Your ways. I believe that I will have what I ask because I walk according to your word. Amen.*

Improve Your Health with Your Tongue

Earlier I talked about how important it is to mind your tongue and speak positively in every situation. I encourage you to talk to God by praying in the Spirit and ask Him to be your personal trainer and to help you in any area in which He knows you are lacking. Speak only the positive and remember this: garbage in—garbage out. Talk to yourself daily and use the name of Jesus in your declarations. Claim your victory in the name of Jesus by utilizing scripture.

When it comes to spiritual things, we can pray it, speak it and can claim it. But when it comes to things that involve the physical, like losing weight, gaining weight, or becoming fit, it seems that Christians get a little lazy. Yes, I said lazy. If we are going to make the necessary changes then it is important that we be honest with ourselves. It's a lot of work to get our bodies in the kind of shape we need them to be in.

Understand one thing: when you're getting your body in shape you are taking care of the place where the Holy Spirit dwells. As you get in better shape you will find yourself needing to pray less in the area of personal health. Like I said earlier, God will answer our prayers but we will still have to do the physical work. I also believe that many Christians need a revelation and a spiritual break-through in this area. Christians are suffering un-necessarily for lack of revelation. They may be over-weight, lethargic, suffer from depression, have high blood pressure, at risk for diabetes, don't feel good about themselves, have back pain, frequent headaches, have trouble sleeping, or are just plain irritable.

All throughout the bible there are stories of individuals who were given something and then they were judged on what they did with that gift. The ones that did not try to multiply their gift and just kept it were not celebrated; they did not sow therefore they did not reap. I believe it to be even more evident when it comes to our bodies. Each one of us has been given a physical body, unique in all different sizes and shapes. I believe we will be judged on how well we have taken care of that gift. "Whether you eat or drink, or whatever you do, do all to the glory of God" (1 Corinthians 10:31).

Are you glorifying God in your body? Don't be too quick to say "Yes." I am not talking about your spiritual walk with God. I am talking about your physical walk with God. Are you working out, trying to eat right, and listening to the Holy Spirit? You know—that little voice that tells you that you have had too much to eat and need to stop. Yes, that same voice you hear that tells you to go witness to this person or go help that person. I believe that same voice speaks to you daily if you are living for God. It will even warn us of things when we're not living for God and we can thank Him for His grace. Practice listening to the prompting of the Holy Spirit when you are about to eat something or when you are being tempted to skip a workout. Listen, then obey.

19

Moderation

What time did you get up this morning? What have you eaten today? Did you do anything physical today? How about this week? Are you satisfied with your day so far? It may seem like I'm asking a lot of questions, and I am, because I want to bring up the point that we all make choices on how we spend our time. We are to be free to be led by the Spirit, not by the latest fad of fashion, diet, or workout routine. We need to get information from God in order to experience the fullness of the wonderful plan He has in store for us.

If we are going to get into condition to serve the Lord, we need to learn to practice moderation in all things. We need to exercise self-restraint in our conversation, our diet, our spending, our time, and in every area of life. Our body was designed to be our servant. We are not to serve its cravings and whims. When it wears out we are going to be in trouble, so we must learn to respect our body and take care of it. Listen to the true messages it sends us—proper nutrition, the need for exercise, ample rest, and active recreation. These are the things our body needs to keep itself in prime working condition.

TIME FOR ACTION

Words are powerful. Think back to some things people have said to you that made you believe in yourself. Maybe there were some things said to you in your childhood that made you feel and believe that you were less than the next person. There is a mind-body connection that is powerful. Some individuals get stuck in an anxious or self-defeating cycle of thinking; they feel like they can never break free. All this distress is from our thoughts. We can be our own worst enemies, but we CAN turn it around by taking charge of our thoughts and words. The wise writer of Proverbs writes, "Death and life are in the power of the tongue..." (Proverbs 18:21). As you complete the questions below, consider how your thoughts and words have affected your life and how you can turn it around by allowing the Holy Spirit to guide your heart and mind...and *words*.

You Need a Revelation

This section of *Balancing the Scales* may be very difficult for some individuals. First, believing that what you believe and tell yourself actually has an impact on your body, mind, and emotions is a hard concept to swallow. Second, sometimes we can be controlled by everything our body, mind, and emotions tell *us*. We become the victim in our quest for fitness. You can tell by the words we might speak. Are you a victim of wrong thinking or speaking negatively?

1. Keep a notepad with you over the next 3 days and mark down how many times you make a negative statement, such as "I can't pass up chocolate" or "I'm not a morning person" or a few choice words at another car during rush hour. Even write down the times you grumble to yourself about your spouse or kids. As soon as you catch yourself speaking a negative, follow it up quickly with a positive. You will see that you will speak fewer negative statements as each day progresses.

   DAY 1:
   Number of negative comments _____

   How easy was it to quickly respond to the negative statements with a positive thought or comment?

   Easy_____   Somewhat Easy_____   Difficult_____

DAY 2:
Number of negative comments _____

How easy was it to quickly respond with a positive thought or comment?

Easy_____   Somewhat Easy_____   Difficult_____

DAY 3:
Number of negative comments _____

How easy was it to quickly respond with a positive thought or comment?

Easy_____   Somewhat Easy_____   Difficult_____

2. What area(s) of negative thought have you found to be the most challenging?

_____
_____
_____
_____
_____
_____
_____
_____
_____
_____

Take Inventory

Getting a realistic view of your self-image is important. Sometimes we dislike a part of our body that we have no power to change; it is a unique aspect of our individuality.

Sometimes we dislike parts that we can change but feel like we have no power to do so.

1. What do you like about your body?

_____
_____
_____
_____

2. How do these attributes make you feel?

_____
_____
_____
_____

3. What do you do to keep these attributes?

_____
_____
_____
_____
_____

4. What do you dislike about your body?

_____
_____
_____
_____
_____

5. How do the things you dislike make you feel?

_____
_____
_____
_____

6. Are the things you dislike within your power to change?

_____

_____

_____

_____

_____

7. What have you been neglecting to do to change the areas you dislike?

_____

_____

_____

_____

_____

8. How are you taking care of the physical resource God has given you (your body)?

_____

_____

_____

_____

_____

9. What 2 steps can you take today to start improving your physical health?

a. _____

_____

_____

b. _____

_____

_____

Take charge of your life and begin working toward making necessary changes. Even more importantly, embrace the unique things about you that you cannot change. Put an end to the negative thoughts and comments about yourself and speak positively about how you were wonderfully and marvelously created to be the best YOU!

One of the Biggest Mistakes

Everything you do to improve your health takes time and consistency. It is important to be patient with yourself. If you mess up and eat a donut, the worst thing you can do is throw your hands up in the air and be frustrated with yourself. What usually happens then is you buy that second donut because you've messed up anyway so you try to feed your frustration by eating more sugar or other comfort food. However, comfort food doesn't comfort for long and you end up feeling worse than when you started. Wouldn't it be better to be patient with yourself and maybe throw out what's ever left of the donut when you realize what you're doing? You didn't blow your healthy eating for the day; you blew it for a mere moment! Get back on that healthy habit saddle and keep on riding.

1. In what situations are you most vulnerable to temptation?

_____

_____

_____

_____

_____

_____

_____

_____

_____

2. How many hours of sleep do you get in a typical night?

_____

3. Do you sleep when you are tired, or do you eat to stay awake? If so, what can you do differently?

_____
_____
_____
_____
_____
_____

Sin or Slip

Reflect on the above questions and, most importantly, your answers. When you have a good idea of your vulnerabilities, answer the following:

1. What action steps can you take to protect yourself from falling into those identified vulnerable situations?

_____
_____
_____
_____
_____
_____
_____

Use some of the Bible verses at the end of the chapters as affirmations. Memorize the scriptures that speak to you and use them as your secret weapon when the temptation to be frustrated arises. By doing this exercise, you will be sowing God's word in your heart that will always produce fruit in your life. There is POWER in the Word.

Improve Your Health by Improving Your Tongue

1. What are some health and vitality issues you are expecting to see change with increased physical activity and fitness?

   _____

   _____

   _____

   _____

   _____

2. How can you align your words with what you are expecting?

   _____

   _____

   _____

   _____

   _____

3. What are some things you need to QUIT saying and some things you COULD say instead?

   _____

   _____

   _____

   _____

   _____

4. Over the past 3 days, could you honestly give thanks to God for all the food you ate? _____

Moderation

Moderation is important in every area of life. We can be assured that we have balance and moderation in life if we spend time asking the Lord for direction. Perhaps God wants you to adjust your schedule or have you train for a 5K run. Perhaps He wants you set aside time for study of His Word.

1. What do you believe the Lord is asking you to do regarding your physical health?

    _____
    _____
    _____
    _____
    _____
    _____
    _____

2. What changes do you believe the Lord is asking you to make to ensure adequate rest?

    _____
    _____
    _____
    _____
    _____

3. What areas of your life do you believe are out of balance?

    _____
    _____
    _____
    _____
    _____

POWER VERSES

Death and life are in the power of the tongue, and those who love it will eat its fruit. Proverbs 18:21

But the Helper, the Holy Spirit, whom the Father will send in my name, He will teach you all things, and bring to your remembrance all that I said to you. John 14:26

I can do all things through Him who strengthens me.
Philippians 4:13

But in all these things we overwhelmingly conquer through
Him who loved us. Romans 8:37

Be of sober spirit, be on the alert. Your adversary, the devil,
prowls around like a roaring lion, seeking someone to
devour. 1 Peter 5:8

Whether, then, you eat or drink or whatever you do, do all
to the glory of God. 1 Corinthians 10:31

RON HENDERSON

CHAPTER THREE

SUPER-CHARGED

Not by might nor by power, but by my spirit says the Lord of hosts. Zechariah 4:6

The good news is that we have a right to be in good shape, to have more energy, and to feel good. Jesus said, "I am come that you might have life and have it more abundantly" (John 10:10). You CAN have an abundant physical life to the extent that God has equipped you. Don't doubt God's promise! Let me break it to you gently: You are not so special that you are the exception and can never stick with a fitness plan. The only thing standing between you and your goals is that organ located between your ears. The good thing is that God is fully aware of this fact and sent us some help if we would only rely on Him. The apostle Paul had to deal with the issue of temptation within the church at Corinth. Let the Word of God be your encouragement:

No temptation has overtaken you but such as is common to man; and God is faithful, who will not allow you to be tempted beyond what you are able, but with the temptation will provide the way of escape also, so that you will be able to endure it. 1 Corinthians 10:13

You are not alone in the temptation department. It is as old as mankind itself. Need I remind you of our ancestors Adam and Eve? But God, in His infinite wisdom, has sent us a Deliverer in His Son, Jesus Christ, and a Helper in the Holy Spirit. With God for us, who can be against us?

Keys to Success

If you are overweight and you are sitting at the dinner table, stuffed from overeating, and you are looking at that pie on the counter, knowing in your heart you shouldn't eat it but you are tempted, what do you do? Well, what do you usually do when you are faced with a temptation? I am not sure what you do, but I begin to pray in the Spirit and focus on the things of God. Some people repeat a verse over and over in their head until they feel the temptation leave them. Then there are times when we all fall a little short. We need to repent and move on with Jesus. You see, there is no temptation common to man that God will not help you, even with overeating.

I believe if you want to be victorious in your quest to lose those unwanted pounds or just to improve overall health, it will be important that you read your bible daily and that you pray without ceasing. Everybody has a stronghold and if you want victory in an area you will need God's help. Then you will have to listen to the Holy Spirit and follow where the Spirit leads you. It will require some physical work. You will have to exercise. You will have to use restraint in your diet.

After I gave my heart to Jesus, I had to read the word daily, pray, and worship God. Many years ago, I had been doing my physical exercises daily but I had been neglecting my spiritual exercises. Because of that neglect, I was suffering spiritually. 3 John 1:2 states, "Beloved, I pray that in all respects you may prosper and be in good health, just as your soul prospers." Through the power of the Holy Spirit within us, we have the power to say no to ourselves and say yes to God, so the fullness of God's plan for us can be manifested in our lives.

If we are to be fit for the service of the Lord and His kingdom we must exercise restraint and self-control. We must discipline our bodies, keeping them under our command and authority. If that means eating less, then you will have to eat less. If it means changing your diet, then you will have to change it. Get resolute and ask Jesus to help you make the changes you desire. Through Christ you CAN do it!

Peeling the Orange

Have you ever eaten an orange? Of course you have. If you were to ask people if they liked oranges, most of them would probably say yes. If you were to ask how many people love sitting down and eating an orange peel, most would probably say no. Life in Christ, in some regards, is like an orange. If you were to scrape off the surface layer and taste it, you would notice a bitter taste and every time you scrape another layer off the orange, the taste gets less bitter until finally you get to the orange wedges where the heart of the orange is and you can see its rich color and taste its succulent juices.

We stand naked before God and when we confess our sins and accept Jesus as our Lord and Savior, He immediately changes our heart and spirit. He gives us peace like we have never known before. Then the Holy Spirit starts to peel away at our outer shell, our walls, and our defenses. As we start to read the Word of God, the Holy Spirit starts to lovingly peel away the layers. As we continue to worship Him more layers come off until He gets us to the point where most

33

people can start to see a difference.

Pay Yourself First

Pay yourself first is one of the basic tips they tell you in the financial world. Take at least 10% of all the money that you earn and set it aside in a savings account. One of the first things you learn in church is to pay God first because it is only by God's grace that we have anything. If you wait to see what you have left in your wallet you may never give God what is rightfully His.

That principle is just as true when it comes to paying yourself physically. Very few of us actually exercise consistently. When we do, it is usually with the time that is left at the end of the day. Yes, we have time for the office, the fund-raising party, the corporate get together, the holiday bash, time to take our significant other out to dinner, and time for the kids, but what about time for us? If we want to have longevity on our side then we must take time out for our health.

Let's be honest, most people are just barely squeezing in their workouts, which is great for beginners because at least they are getting it in. But don't give yourself crumb time. Give yourself prime time. Decide what would be the best time for you to work-out then write the work-out into your schedule. Do not expect to work all day and then come home and have lots of energy to workout. The younger you are when you start a regular fitness program the better off you will be for the long term. By starting early you get your body trained and into the habit of exercising and, if you do fall or have an accident, the rate at which you recover is generally faster. Injury tends to be less traumatic on a body that's in good shape. Why repair damage when you can prevent it?

Don't let age be your excuse for not exercising. I have had clients who have started their fitness training in their 50s, 60s, and 70s and they have achieved amazing results. Christians have a greater motivation to glorify God with their bodies and live a longer, fuller life. When you stay fit and grow in knowledge of the ways of God you gain a strong body and a strong mind because the stronger your body is physically the better you tend to feel mentally.

Recent scientific research has shown that a physically active older person has a decreased risk of dementia. If one should sadly get dementia the extent of it is decreased. I say all this to let you know that your health is worth working for and that the physical dividends you want and need are not far out of your reach. At 65 years of age, I feel like a million dollars. I am the same weight that I was back in 1976. Every year I am approached by people who tell me that I was a motivating factor in them starting a workout program. Now that is money in the bank!

Super-Charged People

Super-charged people are individuals who rely on the power of God through the Holy Spirit to help them through their challenges toward achieving their health and fitness goals. I call them 'super-charged' because they are supernaturally aided by the Holy Spirit to over-come years of bad habits and temptations that seem insurmountable at times. These 'super-charged' folks may be someone you know or that person sitting next to you on the bus or that co-worker who just seems to have a bit more pep in their step and a smile on their face.

My story

There is a myriad of reasons that I could give on why I got in shape and why I stay in shape, but the main reason was that I was so sick and tired of not feeling good physically and mentally. As a high school wrestler, you have to be in great shape. In fact, if you are not in great shape when you start you don't have to worry because the intense training you are put through will get you there. I was feeling good and looking good in no time at all, but as soon as wrestling season ended I did what so many of us often do—I quit working out. Without the immediate need to stay in shape, I quickly went back to my old ways of eating and living. I would stay that way until wrestling season started up again. Then I would repeat the process.

One day I woke up and decided enough is enough. I made myself a promise that as long as I lived, I would never allow myself to get out of shape again. It has been more than 40 years later and I have kept my promise. I have never felt better physically. In fact, there are physical activities that I couldn't do when I was 26 that I can do now that I am 60. I feel super-charged because I allowed the Holy Spirit to transform my heart, my mind, and my will.

More Super-Charged Examples

I am not the only everyday 'super-charged' person out there. Read the stories below of individuals who realized the amazing benefits of living lives 'super-charged':

A Pastor's Story

I began my experience as a senior pastor at 26 years of age. In my late teens until 20 years old I was a trainer at a body building facility. I was in very good shape physically at that point and enjoying good health. That all changed after being married, having two children, and being the leader of a growing ministry. Eating well and exercise became a distant memory. From time to time I may have gone on a run, maybe lifted some weights, yet finding the consistency was difficult. My energy and mental disposition were often compromised by the lack of proper body management.

I will never forget the first time I worked out with Ron Henderson. He noticed that I had good technique and that I had worked out in the past. He asked me, "When was the last time you worked out consistently?" I had to think about that for a moment; then shock. I was 40 years old and it had been 20 years ago! No wonder I was overweight and out of shape! Life had been running me and my family instead of quality daily decisions guiding us. Now, I cannot say that everything changed for the good instantly. I was still very busy and struggled with consistency in this area; yet I did notice a change. Ron's voice in the back of my mind kept reminding me of how important it is to take good care of the only body I will have this side of Heaven. Well, now I am 54 years of age. I went through some tough times that God used to get my attention in this area. I started exercising again just by walking almost every day.

Then the diet...I had a carbohydrate addiction that needed attention. After obtaining some victory in the diet arena, I then started lifting weights a few times per week. I purchased a weighted vest and started doing the stairs at home while wearing it. Then a little running during my walks. The next thing I know, I am at my goal weight, counting my calories and eating as close to source foods as possible! I wish I would have never stopped working out when I was in my early 20's. I wish I would have eaten better quality foods over the years; this would have helped in many areas of my life to do and feel better. Our bodies truly are the temple of the Holy Spirit. I believe God can help us to make powerful decisions about our physical health. He wants to help, yet we need to step out in faith and do something about it. If you do, you will enjoy the results of more energy, flexibility, strength, confidence and a better mental disposition. I am living proof of that! -*Pastor Jay Neu*

A Runner's Story

My journey into fitness was definitely a spiritual journey as well. I was a person who didn't like exercising and I hated sweating. Two good reasons to not do either! I was a normal size for most of my adult life...that was until I hit 40. I gained 60 pounds in two years due to various reasons and I just couldn't seem to lose the weight. One day I felt particularly inspired by the Holy Spirit to run a marathon. I called up a training group and said, "I'm 52, out of shape, and can't even run to my mailbox. Can I train to run a marathon?" The lady on the other end of the phone said, "Sure, you can!" I started training the next week. Each day that passed I added a little more distance. I was so excited that I was actually doing it. Then, with each week that passed, I added more and more miles.

Running became a spiritual experience for me. I prayed while I ran. I listened to worship music. As I felt my strides and the sweat running down my face, I thanked God that I could run; that I could feel this wonderful creation work and move and push itself. It also felt great to go into a sports store with a purpose. I met a whole world of people who are out being active as an integral part of their lives. I smiled when I would tell my friend, "Sorry, I can't stay out any longer. I have a 20-mile run tomorrow morning."

Race day came and I ran with no intention of winning, but I had a fierce desire to accomplish the task before the 6-hour mark. When I finally saw the finish line I was so excited: This 52-year-old woman who couldn't run to the mail box just ran 26.2 miles in 5 hours and 49 minutes.

After this whole experience of training and accomplishing this incredible feat, I realized how important it is to take care of God's creation. There is not a more marvelous creation than our own bodies! We are fearfully and wonderfully made. Pushing myself did more for my persona, mind, and confidence than anything else in my life short of salvation. I know the Lord led me in the adventure.

The experience also shows how powerful our minds can be. If that gal on the other end of the phone would have said, "Well, I don't think you could really do a marathon," I would have never tried. I believed her! My running coach assigned to me told me after I crossed the finish line, "I never thought you could do it." I'm glad she wasn't the one who answered the phone that day. –*Donna H.*

A Soldier's Story

In 2 Timothy 2, the apostle Paul writes to his son in the faith, Timothy, using the words "strong" (v.1), "endure" (v.3), "compete" (v.5) and "hardworking" (v.6). He draws upon the images of a soldier, athlete, and farmer to encourage Timothy to maintain his faith in the days ahead. As a person that spent 30 years in the U.S. Amy with over 10 years in the Infantry, more than 10 years in Army SOF, and five post 9/11 deployments, I am very familiar with those four words when it comes to sustaining the physical conditioning required for success in any situation that I was tasked.

In the context of spiritual warfare that we as Christians are involved with daily, the word pictures that the apostle Paul uses brings to bear the reality of the daily spiritual fight to Timothy. Physical conditioning—much like spiritual training—relates to the needs of the mission, assignment, deployment, or tasking, and needs to be done daily. As the muscle developing concept of "Synaptic Facilitation" (Specificity + Frequent Practice = Success) demands constant usage of the same muscle, doing the same exercise, and then requiring it to do "one more rep" per exercise session. The same applies to a biblical memory program to acquire and place that bible passage into the long-term memory where you will be able to access those verses "in the time of need". In both paradigms, the "muscle memory" on a daily basis helps us to "press toward the mark" (Philippians 3:14) of spiritual and physical fitness.

I went to Basic Combat Training at Fort Jackson, South Carolina. The motto of Fort Jackson is "Victory Starts Here". I have found that to get the victory in my life, either spiritually or physically, I must attend to it early in the day. A psalm that David had written, Psalm 63:1, "God, Thou art my God, early will I seek thee" (KJV) inspires me to seek Him early. I found that starting my day in God's Word aligns my spiritual fitness with His message and strengthens my resolve for those trials that may occur as the day moves forward.

The same goes for my physical fitness. To quote David again, Psalm 113:3, "From the rising of the sun unto the going down of the same the Lord's name is to be praised". Physical training is a technique to praise the Lord. Our body is a "temple" (I Corinthians 3:16-17) and our health is God's blessing to maintain the body for His service (3 John 3). It is our divine tasking from God to maintain our fitness, spiritually and physically. It is our goal to be "deployable" and "operational" for any mission that God our Father assigns us. —*Mark K.*

A Cop's Story

I have been a friend of Ron Henderson, "The Fitness King," for about 30 years. I can honestly say that he is like a brother to me. He reminded me of a conversation we had a long time ago when I was a Minneapolis Police Officer. I made some mistakes, which really screwed up my life, but I managed to make it through. I was telling Ron that I did not think I would live past 45 years of age, so I quit worrying about anything and everything. I just took one day at a time.

As life progressed, I rebuilt my relationship with my children and started to understand what life was all about. I became reactivated in my church, and for the first time in my life, I started to get a real understanding of what it is to have a Father in heaven, a Savior like Jesus Christ, and the Holy Ghost to help me and take care of me. Up to that point I had not taken care of myself physically but only did what I had to do to survive on the streets as a cop.

I was 50 years old when I retired and met my wife, Charlene. It was then that I began to really put the pieces of my life together and, of course, I realized that I was not dead and needed to take better care of myself. I have always looked at Ron as the ultimate example to anyone, but to me in particular, of how to physically take care of yourself. Now, at the age of 75, I am healthy. I'm exercising and have a fantastic relationship with my Father in heaven and my personal Savior Jesus Christ. If this story can be of help to anyone that reads it then I have done something to repay the Lord. —*Richard Stahura*

A Mother's Story

After having 5 children in a span of 7 years, I found myself slowly gaining weight and eating lots of carbs and baking 'treats' for my family as an expression of love. I watched my cholesterol, glucose, and blood pressure begin to rise with each year's annual checkup. After meeting Ron and listening to his gentle encouragement to make small consistent changes in my diet and fitness, I began to understand that God desired me to respect and take care of my physical body in order to have the health and strength I was created to have and be better equipped to be used by God for the tasks and works he created me for.

Now, at age 56, I'm stronger, thinner and more energetic than I've been in years. I am balancing the tasks of life with seeking God daily for spiritual nourishment and nourishing my physical body with good nutrition and exercise. I remember the words of Ron, "Make daily deposits into your health". I thank the Lord for my health and strength as long as He grants it to me. –*Stephanie Schmit*

Time to be Honest

- o Have you accepted the Lord Jesus Christ as your Savior?

- o If not, what is keeping you from accepting the Lord Jesus Christ as your Savior?

- o Are you are living for the Lord or have you fallen away?

- o If you have fallen away, what has caused you to

backslide?

o What is stopping you from getting your heart right with Jesus right now?

Now, take the time to get right with the Lord before you take time to get a right body. You will not only be super-charged in fitness but in every area of your life.

Accountability Contract

"Iron sharpens iron, so one man sharpens another," Proverbs 27:17

The above bible verse works not only in the spiritual realm but also in the physical realm. When two or more people are gathered together with an agreed upon cause and ask the Lord to help and guide them, He is right there in their midst. I have found accountability contracts to be very helpful for anyone that has trouble staying committed to an exercise program or who has trouble controlling their eating. When you draw up a contract—and I do mean draw up—you are not just saying you're going to do something. You are making a firm agreement to keep your promise. Over the years I have seen that the people who had a written contract were more likely to keep it than those that didn't.

When you write up this contract make sure that you do so with someone that will help you keep it. In other words, someone that you trust and that you know will hold you accountable. Someone who is committed to your success and won't let you quit. If you're not used to making these types of contracts, start off with small ones like the example below. You will also have opportunity to draft an accountability contract in the TIME FOR ACTION section at the end of this chapter.

I, _____, commit to workout at least ___ days a week for the next 3 months. I commit to decreasing my food portions by ___%. I commit to reading my bible for at least ___ minutes per day.

Have a beginning and end date to your contract. Add whatever you know you can honestly commit to doing. Then, after you complete your contract, create another. You will quickly find that it gets easier and easier to complete and keep your contracts. After each contract that you complete make sure that you thank Jesus for giving you the victory, then thank your accountability partner for their support.

Rest

In this crazy world we live in most of us are so busy thinking about our business affairs, family life, and retirement, that we have a hard time relaxing, let alone getting adequate sleep. Sleep is one of the most important things we need in order for our body to function at its highest level. Depending on your lifestyle, the amount you need can vary. The quality of our sleep is equally as important as the quantity. When we are out of balance in our lives, we may find ourselves tossing and turning instead of getting restful, restorative sleep. That's where exercise and prayer comes in. People who exercise tend to sleep better and wake up more rested. If you're having trouble sleeping, ask God to give you a sanctified sleep. In fact, God promises in his Word to give you a sweet sleep. Ask in faith and receive what is yours. In reality, everything in this book is based on activating your faith. Now activate it and sleep, sleep, sleep.

But I'm in Great Shape!

If you're in great shape, then you're probably reading this book by accident...at least that is what you're thinking. Well, my friend, there are no accidents. God has predestined each and every one of us before the world began to increase in faith and the grace He freely offers. So, if you're still reading then this section is for you. Maybe you're the opposite of the average reader. Maybe you're in great shape but you are spiritually a wreck. You seek happiness in everything but God. You can search and search but you will never find true peace unless it is in Christ Jesus.

I did everything I could to try and be happy only to end up feeling completely empty on the inside. It is easy for people like us to workout. We've done it for most of our lives. But surrender all to Jesus? That's the hard part. Yet, it is truly the most rewarding experience. You see, most of my adult life I wanted to serve Jesus, but it just seemed like no matter how much I tried I would slip right back into my old life.

Maybe that's you. If you want victory in this life and you are not sure how to get it, take the initiative and go to your pastor or anyone who believes in the gifts of the Spirit and ask them to pray with you and deal with any wrong influences in your spirit. If you have an area in your life that you just can't seem to get victory in, trust me, you probably have some wrong influences at work. Sometimes these can be generational spirits passed down from your parents and sometimes it can be from things you were involved with in the past. Whatever spirits or influences that have attached themselves to you, you need to have prayer in the name of Jesus—the name above all other names.

Once this is done, you need to read the word, pray,

worship God, and, with the help of the Holy Spirit, strive to live a holy life. You may not be perfect and you may slip up not meaning to, but God's children do not continually sin. Deuteronomy 30:19 reads, "I have set before you life and death, the blessing and the curse. So choose life." Well, my friend, which do you choose?

Spiritually Fit but Physically Broken

My heart hurts when I see Christians who are spiritually fit but who are in poor physical health. My desire is to help people realize that they are short-changing themselves physically by neglecting their bodies and to help them reprioritize some things in their lives and the lives of their families. There is more to this life than just living only to grow old and find that the quality of our physical lives has been greatly diminished due to our lack of concern for our health.

As a personal trainer with over 30 years of experience, I have noticed that the average man or woman over 50 does not participate in any kind of an exercise program and is in poor physical shape. The condition of our body, just like our spiritual life, is based on what we do. We have all been told to work out, eat right, and so on. Some of us do these things but we were never really given a plan with our later years in mind. My father, whom I love dearly, although in his early 90s, is in great physical shape—and not because of heredity. It is because he has worked out almost religiously for the last 20 years. In fact, I remember watching my father work out and thinking to myself, you are wasting your time and you are going to get hurt. So I asked my father if he would mind if I helped him with his workouts. He agreed and, in a short period of time I could see his body begin to be more defined. Not only was he looking different but he was feeling better.

As a personal trainer, I am always preaching that nothing

beats correct technique. If you don't train correctly you'll never look the way you want and you are more likely to injure yourself. My father, with his thoughts on tomorrow, made a physical commitment to his health and family by setting a good example. The same way most of us have been taught by our parents to save money and invest wisely, he made one of the best investments he will ever make—his health.

When you think about it, most Christians prepare for life on earth and life in heaven by living according to the Word of God. Although we can't determine a family member's life span or even our own, we can decide what the quality of our families physical and spiritual lives will be. By raising our children with godly examples they have every opportunity to accept Jesus Christ as their Lord and Savior. Some of us prepare financially by saving money for ourselves and our children's future. But what about their physical and spiritual futures? Are we setting good examples for them to follow?

"Or do you not know that your body is a temple of the Holy Spirit who is in you, whom you have from God, and that you are not your own?" 1 Corinthians 6:19

TIME FOR ACTION

Do you want to be super-charged? Jesus said, "I am come that you might have life and have it more abundantly" (John 10:10 KJV). An abundant life is a super-charged one. You can have abundance in every area of your life. It starts with believing that what Jesus said is true. By believing in and trusting in the help of the Holy Spirit for your physical and emotional health, you begin the journey of being led by the Spirit, and that brings about LIFE!

Keys to Success

Temptation will confront you whenever you are trying to make steps in a positive direction. It is not a sin to be tempted but temptation can lead us into sin and a fruitless outcome. Knowing that temptation is inevitable, having a plan to resist is imperative.

1. What do you usually do when faced with temptation? Write down at least three responses then rate them as to their effectiveness.

   _____
   _____
   _____
   _____
   _____
   _____

2. What could you start doing differently to help you resist temptation?

   _____
   _____
   _____
   _____
   _____
   _____

3. What areas of your life need more discipline?

   _____
   _____
   _____
   _____
   _____
   _____

4. What responses to temptation will you commit to using over the next week?

_____

_____

_____

_____

_____

_____

Pay Yourself First

When your health and fitness is the last thing you think about during the day or something you keep putting off time and again you are not paying yourself first. In fact, you are barely giving yourself crumbs. You can't be at your physical, emotional, and mental peak when you put exercise and healthy living on the bottom of your to-do list. At some point you have to make it one of your top priorities.

1. What keeps you from making daily exercise a priority?

_____

_____

_____

_____

_____

_____

2. What are some action steps you can take to help you address the issues listed in question one?

_____

_____

_____

_____

_____

_____

3. Consciously take the action steps in question two and apply them to your life over the next three days. Write down how they helped you to prioritize exercise.

_____
_____
_____
_____
_____
_____

Super-Charged People

Super-charged people are individuals who rely on the power of God through the Holy Spirit to help them through their challenges. Being around these people can be inspiring as well as educational.

1. Do you know a super-charged person? How can you learn from them?

_____
_____
_____
_____
_____
_____

Time to be Honest

It is time to be honest with yourself. Write down your answers to the questions that follow. I want you to do this exercise to record your thoughts for your reflection. Be honest. You and the Lord are the only ones that need to see what you have written. If you feel open to sharing with others in your study group go ahead and do so. Your journey of faith and honest answers may be an encouragement to others.

1. Have you accepted the Lord Jesus Christ as your Savior?

   _____

2. If you answered 'no' in question 1, what is keeping you from accepting the Lord Jesus Christ as your Savior?

   _____

   _____

   _____

   _____

   _____

3. Are you living for the Lord or have you fallen away?

   _____

   _____

   _____

   _____

   _____

4. If you have fallen away, what has caused you to backslide?

   _____

   _____

   _____

   _____

   _____

5. What is stopping you from getting your heart right with Jesus right now?

   _____

   _____

   _____

   _____

   _____

Take the time to get right with the Lord before you take time to get a right body. You will not only be super-charged in fitness but in every area of your life.

Accountability Contract

Are you ready for an accountability contract? When you are serious about reaching health and fitness goals, an accountability contract with someone who will hold you accountable is an excellent tool for success. Your contract should be **specific** (what you are committing to do), **realistic** (what you can reasonably accomplish at this time) and **measurable** (start date and end date; how will you measure the contract so you can tell when you have accomplished the contract?) Write your contract below and refer to it often throughout its duration.

My Accountability Contract

_____

_____

_____

_____

_____

_____

_____

_____

_____

_____

_____

_____

_____

_____

_____

_____

_____

_____

Rest

Rest is as important to our health as drinking water. A person can last 3-4 weeks without food, only 3-4 days without water, and approximately 11 days without sleep. It will not be pleasant during those 11 days for you or anyone around you! In fact, it can be deadly. For your body to work optimally you need a good amount of uninterrupted sleep every night (approximately 7-8 hours).

Sleep Log

Complete the sleep log below:

Day & Date	Activity 2 hours prior to bedtime	Time Asleep	Time Awake	Total Hours of Sleep
Day 1:				
Day 2:				
Day 3:				
Day 4:				
Day 5:				
Day 6:				
Day 7:				

Review your sleep log. Are there any changes you need to make to your sleep behaviors? Make the adjustments and complete a second sleep log below:

Day & Date	Activity 2 hours prior to bedtime	Time Asleep	Time Awake	Total Hours of Sleep
Day 1:				
Day 2:				
Day 3:				
Day 4:				
Day 5:				
Day 6:				
Day 7:				

POWER VERSES

The thief comes only to steal and kill and destroy; I came that they may have life, and have it abundantly."
John 10:10

No temptation has overtaken you but such as is common to man; and God is faithful, who will not allow you to be tempted beyond what you are able, but with the temptation will provide the way of escape also, so that you will be able to endure it. 1 Corinthians 10:13

Beloved, I pray that in all respects you may prosper and be in good health, just as your soul prospers. 3 John 1:2

Iron sharpens iron, so one man sharpens another.
Proverbs 27:17

I call heaven and earth to witness against you today, that I have set before you life and death, the blessing and the curse. So choose life in order that you may live, you and your descendants, Deuteronomy 30:19

Or do you not know that your body is a temple of the Holy Spirit who is in you, whom you have from God, and that you are not your own? 1 Corinthians 6:19

CHAPTER FOUR

MIND, WORD, AND BODY

*Be not deceived; God is not mocked: for whatsoever a
man soweth, that shall he also reap.*
Galatians 6:7

In my lifetime I have met, known, and observed many
Christians and even pastors who cared very little for their
health. They loved God, prayed, read the bible, spoke in
tongues, and witnessed to others, but as far as taking care
of their bodies (or should I say God's body) they seemed to
fall considerably short. They would talk about eating too
much at the church socials and potluck dinners or holiday
parties. At the start of every year they would do what a lot of
us do and make another New Year's resolution that they will
never keep. At least that's the way it appears. They never
really realized how much more they could do for God if they
took better care of themselves.

By this point in the book you are probably thinking,
"Alight already, Fitness King. You are preaching to the choir."
Well, if you have done away with your old pattern of taking
care of the 'temple' God has given you then I applaud you!

But this is the point when you really must keep on your guard. About the time we think we have it down pat we step into a trap. Hold on now...we can't blame the devil for everything. Usually the trap comes from our own thinking, speaking, or doing.

God has set a principle in the earth called *sowing and reaping*. We see this principle active every day in nature, relationships, and the practical matters of life. You plant a seed and a seedling pops up from the ground. You nurture your relationships and they grow deeper. You put in the time and effort to excel at your job and you get a promotion. The flip side is true, too. You put bad seed in bad ground and no matter how much rain or sun it receives, you never see it break through the dirt. You sow discord in your relationships and you end up in conflict and possibly without any friends. You show up late to work and slack off during the day and you end up in the unemployment line.

Let's look at our key verse and those that follow (Galatians 6:7-9):

> 7 "Do not be deceived, God is not mocked; for whatever a man sows, this he will also reap. 8 For the one who sows to his own flesh will from the flesh reap corruption, but the one who sows to the Spirit will from the Spirit reap eternal life. 9 Let us not lose heart in doing good, for in due time we will reap if we do not grow weary.

God is giving us the heads-up in verse 7 by letting us know we may be deceived regarding His principles. We can be led astray or taken off course by someone's opinion or our own thoughts. To be deceived in this case is to bring havoc onto ourselves. The word *mocked* means to turn your nose up at someone or to not take them seriously, but laughingly disregard what they have to say or who they are.

God is telling us that he takes his principle seriously and will not be snickered at by those who think this principle does not apply to him or herself. That is like saying gravity only applies to certain people. But how many of us eat like the empty calories won't have an effect on our waistline? Or that another greasy hamburger and fries won't clog our arteries and put us at risk for heart disease? God says that *whatever* a man (or woman) sows he will also reap accordingly. No exceptions. No free pass. That puts our every action in a new light.

I challenge you to spend the next 24 hours taking these verses into consideration with everything you do. At the end of that time ask yourself, "Did I do anything different because of God's word regarding sowing?" I think you may be surprised. Just think how different your life would be if you lived by these words from God.

God's word states that our reaping may not be an instant reward or punishment, whichever the case may be. He says it may take some time. Have you ever wondered how some people can steal, murder, and create mayhem but never seem to pay the price for their evil doings? It may be especially bothersome if you have been playing by the rules and doing what you know is good and right to do, but it seems like you just can't get ahead. God's Word encourages you to be patient and don't become tired of doing good because, in due time, you will reap your harvest. The same holds true in your quest to be healthy and fit. Persevere! Hang in there! Keep on truckin'! Your efforts will pay off in vitality, endurance, strength, and a toned body.

I have found that there are three areas in which the principle of sowing and reaping are especially influential for fitness and faith: sowing with your mind, sowing with your words, and sowing with your body. God wants all of you. He wants your mind, body, and spirit in the days ahead as you get into the habit of training your body along with exercising your mind. You will notice you have more energy to teach longer, to preach longer, to pray longer, and to focus better. Let's look at each area more closely.

Sowing with Your Mind

Many years ago, I remember wishing there was a pill I could take to help me walk closer with God; I just never seemed able to keep myself from falling short or sinning. Well, I knew there wasn't a pill then and there is not a pill now. There will never be one. There is only one way to walk with Jesus and that is to give him your heart, body, mind and soul. The reason I could never really have a consistent walk with Jesus was because I had so much garbage in my mind from being exposed to pornography and premarital sex early on in my life. The devil had a foothold on me. I had never dealt with those spirits even though I had confessed my sins. Within a month or two after repenting I would slip back into my old life. "If they only had a pill," I would often repeat. My spirit was willing, but my flesh was indeed weak.

There are a variety of weight loss pills on the market all promising to help you lose weight and control your appetite. In many cases they will help you take off those unwanted pounds, but at what risk? Most pills on the market are not safe and remember, there are no panaceas. The only way to takeoff weight and keep it off is to develop a lifestyle that involves exercise and common sense eating. This is easy to say but it is hard to do for most people. I'm here to tell you it can be done in your life and will be done by the grace of God. Just like the stronghold sexual sin had over me, some of you have the stronghold of appetite keeping you from being completely free in Jesus. I can tell you from experience that confession, prayer, resisting the tricks of the enemy of your soul, and rebuking the devil's influence in your mind, all lead to victory. As I have been set free, so can you. All things are possible through Jesus Christ. Renew your mind to have godly thoughts. Fill your heart and mind with the Word of God. Let your mind rehearse scripture instead of the latest secular tune or advertisement jingle. You'll experience the joy of being free from those sins that bound you.

The youth pastor who led me to Jesus used to always sing an old gospel song, *"...only believe, only believe, all things are possible if you only believe..."* If you truly believe then you are resolute in your mind. If you are resolute in your mind then you will most likely carry out actions that line up with your mind. Have you ever made a decision that you are not really sure was the right one? You may have been nervous or a bit tenuous in your actions. If you start an exercise plan not sure if you're going to be able to follow through then you most likely will not. If you approach a healthy eating plan mourning over the donut you can't have then you will most likely not stay on that plan for long. Why? You are defeated in your mind before you even begin.

When you first decide to change how you eat you will be tempted every time you sit down at the table. You have to approach your temptation to food the same way you approach any other temptation. One of the first things to do is remember that there is no temptation common to man that he will not provide a way to escape (1 Corinthians 10:13). Get that in your mind and in your spirit. Then you must do your part by resisting temptation and looking for the way of escape. Your way of escape may be calling your accountability partner, engaging in a task, an unexpected visitor, or taking a bite out of an apple instead of the pastry. Your door of escape might even be the door! The more you resist, the easier fleeing temptation will become until, at last, what you thought was a major stronghold in your life will be like a mere speck.

Anything that you allow to control you will have you bound. Many people pacify themselves with food. It is their 'happy place.' Why do you think there is so much 'comfort food' out there? We get used to having that sugar high or caffeine energy. We almost become comatose after a huge feast. If we are using food to pacify ourselves then we must look at our souls and ask, "What am I not giving to God to satisfy?" Food, drugs, or anything else is a sorry substitute for the peace of mind the Lord provides if we simply allow Him to do so. Sometimes people gorge themselves because they don't know what else to do. They will never be happy letting food control them just as I was never happy being controlled by the lust of my flesh.

When I stopped feeding my flesh and when I started to really resist is when things started to spiritually change in those areas of my life. It can be the same for you. Make the commitment to control what you put into your mouth. Even if it's a little change here and a little change there, eventually you will have victory in those areas of your life. Let the verse 1 Corinthians 6:12 be your mantra:

All things are lawful for me, but not all things are profitable. All things are lawful for me, but I will not be mastered by anything.

It would serve you well to memorize some if not all of the bible verses at the end of this chapter. Let them spring up in your moments of temptation as they just may be a door of escape right when you need one.

Sowing with Your Words

Take an inventory of what you say one day. Make a mental note of every negative comment that comes out of your mouth. Better yet, let someone else take account of anything negative that you say. You may be surprised! Negative words are like seeds; you plant them and they grow into all sorts of weeds. As I said earlier, waking up with a sniffle and saying, "I'm coming down with a cold," will almost guarantee that you will spend the next two weeks with a drippy nose, coughing, and sneezing. This is not a name-it-and-claim-it phenomena but a declaration of how the sniffle will progress. Your mind believed what came out of your mouth. The sniffle might have been due to dry air or any host of reasons. Here's another example: Someone at work brings in fresh donuts for everyone. You say, "Oh my goodness, they look so good, but I can't eat one because I'm on this diet." You just gave your mind a reason to free you from the injustice of being deprived the sugary treat. A better response would be, "No, thank you. I am just too happy about my slimming waistline and clean arteries to blow it all on the fleeting flavor of empty calories." Now, you may not make too many office buddies saying that, but your body will thank you.

Unlike negative seeds, which lead you into frustration, sickness, and failure, positive seeds bring about positive results. If you want to change your harvest you'll need to change the words you speak. Positive seeds are anything you say that goes along with the Word of God and anything that builds you up spiritually. Speaking life over yourself and your situation will help your seeds of success to grow. I make it a practice to quote scripture to myself whenever I encounter difficulties because the Word of God is living and sharp as a double-edge sword (Hebrews 4:12). Not only that, but "kind words are like honey – sweet to the soul and healthy for the body" (Proverbs 16:24). Take the time to speak scripture over your situation and see the hand of God move on your behalf.

If I am going to improve my body and my mind, I must sow the positive by speaking the positive. Statements such as, *I thank the Lord that I have control over eating and my eating no longer has control over me*, can go a long way in helping you stay in control of your eating. Start declaring right now that you can do all things through Jesus Christ who strengthens you (Philippians 4:13). As you keep speaking the positive, your seed will continue to grow. Don't give up, but persevere until you reap your harvest.

It is not what goes into the mouth that defiles a person, but what comes out of the mouth; this defiles a person.
Matthew 15:11

Sowing with Your Body

When you grow up in an environment that teaches you that money is the root of all evil and that taking care of yourself is vanity, you can clearly see why people develop guilt in those areas. The bible says the *love* of money is the root of all evil (1 Timothy 6:10). It does not say having money is evil. Being concerned with how you look and feel is not a sin either. In fact, it is clearly stated in the bible that God wants you to prosper and be in good health (3 John 1:2). Never-the-less, there are many Christians who use the vanity issue as an excuse not to do what they know they should be doing.

If we spent even half the time exercising rather than making excuses on why we don't exercise most of us would be in good shape. You can fast and pray all day long, but you cannot expect God to perform a miracle in an area that does not need a miracle. God gives us a choice—sit on the couch and stay sick and tired or get up and get moving. Go for a brisk walk when you don't feel like it. Skip those French Fries and choose the broccoli. Take the stairs instead of the elevator. I believe God wants and expects us to do our part. God expects you to exercise if you physically can and to take care of your body. God does not want or need our excuses on why we don't exercise. He needs our commitment to take care of everything he has bestowed upon us.

It is important to realize that no matter how much we talk about our weight it will not just magically melt away. It will take some hard work. Sowing into anything worthwhile isn't always easy. The farmer has to go out into his field and pick out all the rocks. Then the hard surface of the field needs to be tilled to prepare it to accept the seed. The seed must then be placed into the ground, covered, watered, and nurtured by the sunlight. Ask any farmer if his or her job is easy. They will certainly say no.

Remember when you were first saved and how you felt? The peace you first received was so amazing. Then you found out that to keep this peace required you to go to work spiritually by reading the Word, praying, and praising God. If you stopped doing even one of these disciplines you found yourself slowly slipping back into your old lifestyle. Well, working out is much the same. You can start with good intention, but if you want to succeed you will have to make a true commitment. Start sowing now by asking the Lord Jesus Christ to give you the strength to say no to overeating and yes to daily exercise. In 1 Corinthians 9:27 Paul writes, "But I discipline my body and bring it into subjection, lest, when I have preached to others I myself should become disqualified." In short—practice what you preach. Sow good actions and keep at it. Don't expect the harvest tomorrow but be like the farmer who understands the hard work, patience, and the meaning of seasons.

Throughout the bible it is evident that God wants us to prosper and be in good health. If we know this then we understand that there is nothing wrong with going out and enjoying a nice meal. The problem is that we have been conditioned to overeating. There are very few Sundays that I remember not having gone out for lunch after church with friends. To tell you the truth, most of the time I over-ate like so many people do. Because I have been diligent on taking care of myself and am in great shape, I was able to say that I could afford to overeat. Yet, realistically speaking, I should not be overeating and neither should you.

We all need to listen to that little voice that says, *stop...you've had enough*. Remember, anything that controls you is not of God and is taking the place of God in your life. If you want victory in your addiction to food you must capture every thought and every imagination. Do not live to eat, rather eat so you might live. Live to glorify God in your body and in your spirit. "For him that knows to do good, and doeth it not to him it is sin" (James 4:17). If you can't physically afford to over-eat, then don't. Take control of your thoughts and when you feel like overeating satisfy yourself by reading the Word of God. That is the only food of which you can never get too much.

Sadly, if you choose to disrespect your body through neglect and abuse you will reap the consequences. You can't expect to eat what you want and do what you want and not pay a penalty. All life is precious and must be treated that way. If you eat one fat laden meal after another you are at a greater risk of developing high cholesterol. If you smoke pack after pack of cigarettes, don't be surprised if you get lung cancer. If you carry around more weight than your body was designed to carry, don't be surprised if you have sore hips, sore knees, and maybe even a heart attack. These are but a few of the things that put stress on your body and are totally unnecessary. Sow wisely! If you eat right and stay on a consistent exercise program don't be surprised when you have more energy, that you sleep better, look better, have more stamina, and are even more pleasant. Decide right now what you want to look like and what you want to feel like and sow accordingly.

Creating Distance

If you want to succeed in the spiritual realm you will need to eliminate those things you know to be sin. Eradicate them from your life because they will cause you to pull away from God. The same applies to the physical body. If you are having trouble eating right then you need to resist those foods. In fact, keep them away from you. Don't allow foods you know aren't good for your body in your house because you will eventually consume it. Food, for some, is a sin because they are controlled by it. You cannot play games in any area of your life that has been a problem to you. You will always reap what you have sown in the spirit or in the body. As God's children living in these earthen vessels, our bodies will atrophy if we neglect them. So, if we desire to live a longer and healthier life, we will have to protect and preserve our most valuable asset—our body.

There is no temptation taken you but such   is common to man: but God is faithful, who   will not suffer you to be tempted above that ye are able: but will with the temptation also make away to escape, that ye may be able to bear it."
1 Corinthians 10:13

TIME FOR ACTION

The law of sowing and reaping is a common theme in nature and Christianity. The beginning of this chapter puts forth a challenge to spend 24 hours pondering Galatians 6:7-9 (sowing and reaping) and at the end of that time ask yourself, "Did I do anything different because of God's word regarding sowing?"

Write your observations below:

_____

_____

_____

_____

_____

_____

_____

_____

_____

_____

_____

_____

Sowing with Your Mind

So much of what we do starts in the mind. We know the consequences of making bad decisions. We have given in to impulses without thinking of the long-term effects. If you are unsure that you can change your bad habits you're setting yourself up for failure. If you are mourning over the donuts and ice cream you should be cutting back on, then you will likely not stay on a healthier eating plan. Remember, in all temptations, the Lord has provided a way of escape. Believe it!

1. What is your go-to comfort food?

_____

_____

_____

_____

_____

_____

2. What healthy replacement food could you substitute for this comfort food while you are working through the issues of why you are turning to food for satisfaction?

_____

_____

_____

_____

_____

3. If turning to food for comfort is a problem for you, with whom can you partner to help you work through this ineffectual pattern?

_____

_____

_____

Sowing with Your Words

If you absolutely believed that all your words bring forth fruit—good or bad—you would most likely be very careful with what you say. Some words that you sow may take years to produce results. Maybe you know someone who was told their whole life that they were never going to amount to anything. That seed of negativity was sown in their mind and spirit and now that person struggles with self-image and may believe their potential is limited. Then think of kids who grew up with lots of positive affirmation. As adults they are more likely to live out that positivity. Search your heart.

1. Are there negative comments that have stuck with you? Write them down and then release them to God.

_____

_____

_____

_____

_____

Lord, I release the hurt from the negative comments that have been spoken about my life and the negative effects of those comments. I receive Your word that I am fearfully and wonderfully made. In the name of Jesus, Amen.

2. Have you spoken negative comments about others or about your own life?

    a. Repent of the negative comments and receive forgiveness. Ask for God's help to redeem your words to speak truth and positivity.

    b. Confess the sin of speaking negativity about others. Ask those you may have harmed with your words for forgiveness and see the hand of the Lord work in their hearts and yours.

Sowing with Your Body

There is an old saying, "You are what you eat." That is another statement that reflects the principle of sowing and reaping. Sowing and reaping isn't a one-time deal. It is a long-term commitment. 1 Corinthians 7:27 states, "I discipline my body and bring it into subjection, lest, when I have preached to others I myself should become disqualified.

1. How do you need to bring your body into subjection?

_____
_____
_____
_____
_____
_____
_____
_____
_____

2. When you eat snacks or meals, what percentage of the
time are you actually feeling hungry? Explain:

_____

_____

_____

_____

_____

3. If you eat when you are hungry, what percentage of the
time do you not eat once you are no longer hungry?

_____

_____

_____

_____

_____

_____

Creating Distance

Putting distance between you and danger is prudent. Putting
distance between you and temptation is necessary if it is too
easy for you to give in. You may have to throw that carton of
ice cream in the trash or postpone that cup of coffee in the
morning and get right on the exercise bike. You can't always
get rid every temptation, but if you do it where and when you
can, you will be better able to accomplish your goals.

I can create distance by:

_____

_____

_____

_____

_____

_____

_____

POWER VERSES

Do not be deceived, God is not mocked; for whatever a man sows, this he will also reap. For the one who sows to his own flesh will from the flesh reap corruption, but the one who sows to the Spirit will from the Spirit reap eternal life. Let us not lose heart in doing good, for in due time we will reap if we do not grow weary. Galatians 6:7-9

No temptation has overtaken you but such as is common to man: and God is faithful, who will not allow you to be tempted beyond what you are able, but with the temptation will provide the way of escape also, so that you will be able to endure it. 1 Corinthians 10:13

All things are lawful for me, but not all things are profitable. All things are lawful for me, but I will not be mastered by anything. 1 Corinthians 6:12

For as he thinks within himself, so he is. Proverbs 23:7a

And do not be conformed to this world, but be transformed by the renewing of your mind, so that you may prove what the will of God is, that which is good and acceptable and perfect. Romans 12:2

The steadfast of mind You will keep in perfect peace, because he trusts in You. Isaiah 26:3

For God has not given us a spirit of timidity, but of power and love, and discipline. 2 Timothy 1:7

For though we walk in the flesh, we do not war according to the flesh, for the weapons of our warfare are not of the flesh, but divinely powerful for the destruction of fortresses. We are destroying speculations and every lofty thing raised up against the knowledge of God, and we are taking every thought captive to the obedience of Christ, and we are ready to punish all disobedience, whenever your obedience is complete. 2 Corinthians 10:3-6

For the word of God is living and active and sharper than any two-edged sword and piercing as far as the division of soul and spirit, of both joints and marrow, and able to judge the thoughts and intentions of the heart.
Hebrews 4:12

Pleasant words are a honeycomb, sweet to the soul and healing to the bones. Proverbs 16:24

I can do all things through Him who strengthens me.
Philippians 4:13

It is not what enters the mouth that defiles the man, but what proceeds out of the mouth, this defiles the man.
Matthew 15:11

For the love of money is a root of all sorts of evil, and some by longing for it have wandered away from the faith and pierced themselves with many griefs. 1 Timothy 6:10

But I discipline my body and make it my slave, so that, after I have preached to others, I myself will not be disqualified. 1 Corinthians 9:27

Therefore, to one who knows the right thing to do and does not do it, to him it is sin. James 4:17

CHAPTER FIVE

CAPTURING THE VISION

Then the LORD answered me and said,
"Record the vision and inscribe it on tablets,
That the one who reads it may run."
Habakkuk 2:2

Let's face it, it's a great feeling to be able to go into your closet and grab just about anything and know it will look great on you. Do you have a myriad of clothes in your closet that you can't wear? If you do, you are like so many men and woman who go year after year with the thought in the back of their mind that someday they will lose that unwanted weight and to be able to wear those clothes that are stuffed in the back of their closet. Unfortunately, for many that day never comes. As the years go by, you find it even harder to fit into the clothes that are on your back, let alone being able to fit into the clothes you have saved for the day you lose a size or two. We become even more complacent in regard to our lack of care for our physical bodies. We go to church every Sunday; we sing in the church choir or we might even be a pastor. We may be totally sold out to Jesus spiritually but have our body in our own control. Let's reflect upon 1 Corinthians 6:19:

75

Do you not know that your body is the temple of the Holy Spirit who is in you, whom you have from God, and you are not your own? For you were bought at a price, therefore let us glorify God in your body and in your spirit, which are God's.

I wear the same size clothes I did when I was 25 years old. I'm not bragging but telling you this to prove that this isn't impossible! It is within your grasp. You can do it! You can have the fit and toned body that you have wanted for so long! Are you feeling a little bit excited? You should!

People Perish for Lack of Vision

Take a moment and visualize what you think you'll look like fit and healthy. Get detailed. How will you stand? What clothes will you wear? How will those clothes fit? Picture what you will be doing when you are fit. Will you be playing tennis or taking long, invigorating walks? Now think about how it will feel when your clothes will fit nicely and how much fun you are going to have buying that new wardrobe. What sports might you want to get involved in now that you are in shape? Think about where you might want to go when you are not restricted by lack of energy or back problems from carrying around too much body weight. See yourself playing with your kids outside, running with them, going down the slide, biking, skiing, etc. Get a vision! Ponder that vision for at least 5 minutes. Picture yourself slim and fit every day. Keep that picture in your mind.

Have you ever noticed the shape of people who frequent ice cream stands or greasy food carts? Recently, I was at the beach and had the opportunity to observe an ice cream treat vending machine and the only people in line were children and obese adults. There wasn't a slim adult anywhere near the machine. Then I took stock of who drinks diet soda, and again, mostly overweight men and women. The healthy and fit folks were engaged in physical activities and interacting with their children. Instead of soda they had bottled water in their hands. They ran on the beach and were buoyant in their stride. They laughed louder and smiled more often.

Now, go back to that vision of the trim and toned you. Close your eyes and picture yourself on the beach. What would the trim you do? What would you feel like? Most of us know the popular saying, "What would Jesus do?" I am asking, "What would trim Gladys do?" "What would trim Mark do?" "What would trim (fill in your name) do?" You may surprise yourself with what you imagine you would do and what choices you would make.

Practice imagining this new you when you encounter the temptation to indulge in foods that you struggle saying no to or when you don't want to get off of the couch. Would you be doing such things as a trim person? Unleash the you that is trying to escape years of overeating and a sedentary lifestyle! And don't stop at simply visualizing. Thank God for your health and strength. Thank Him that you have the ability to change and be the person He has created you to be. Give God praise for you are wonderfully and marvelously made! He has said that you are more than a conqueror (Romans 8:37).

The Importance of Laughter

Researchers have found that fifteen minutes of laughing is the equivalent to five minutes of moderate jogging. Think back to the last time you had a good belly laugh. Your stomach and sides probably hurt afterward. You had tears in your eyes and could barely stand up straight. You were probably out of breath as well. Laughing is good aerobics!

I encourage you to treat laughter the way you do drinking

water. Get as much in as you can. Surround yourself with people who love to laugh. Some people can lighten a room by simply walking into it. They have a gift of laughter and bringing joy to any situation they are in. These people are invaluable in reminding us to smile, to laugh, and to enjoy life. Remember those times you were feeling down and one person smiled at you. Sometimes a smile can make your day. Laughter has many health benefits. Sick people who laugh tend to recover more quickly. It can make you look younger and it can burn calories. Face it, laughter makes you feel good all over.

A merry heart doeth good like a medicine:
but a broken spirit drieth the bones. Proverbs 17:22

TIME FOR ACTION

Are you in it for the long haul? That can seem like a daunting question. A healthy and fit lifestyle is just that...*a lifestyle!* Capture the vision of you being able to resist that piece of chocolate because you have a bigger picture of fitness in mind. Capture the vision of excitement when getting up a bit early on your day off, so you can go outside and take a brisk walk. Capture the vision of sitting down and still being able to breathe because your pants aren't too tight. Capture the vision of feeling good about your health, body, and choices you are making. As you are working towards changing your lifestyle remember to keep that vision fresh in your mind. Picture you being older and able to keep up with the grandkids, or being able to garden, travel, go dancing, or being active all day. Now that you have that picture in your mind, make the daily choices that will make that picture a reality.

People Perish for Lack of Vision

Close your eyes and try to picture yourself trim and healthy.
What would you be doing? What would today look like if you
had energy and vigor? Take 5 minutes right now and get that
vision clear in your mind.

1. Were there any differences between your image and your
   present?

   _____
   _____
   _____
   _____
   _____

2. You have made progress during this study in the
   following areas evidenced by:

   _____
   _____
   _____
   _____
   _____

3. How has your purpose changed since the first chapter of
   Balancing the Scales, if at all?

   _____
   _____
   _____
   _____
   _____

The Importance of Laughter

Sometimes we can be too serious. After all, life is serious
business! However, as the old adage says, "All work and no
play makes Johnny a dull boy." Give yourself permission to

laugh. Laughter has an incredible amount of health benefits. Make sure you laugh heartily and often. If you are working through this study guide with a group, share a funny story and let yourself laugh. If you are working through this individually, share a funny story with someone this week and enjoy the laughter.

POWER VERSES

Then the Lord answered me and said,
"Record the vision and inscribe it on tablets, that the one who reads it may run. Habakkuk 2:2

Or do you not know that your body is a temple of the Holy Spirit who is in you, whom you have from God, and that you are not your own? 1 Corinthians 6:19

But in all these things we overwhelmingly conquer through Him who loved us. Romans 8:37

A joyful heart is good medicine, but a broken spirit dries up the bones. Proverbs 17:22

CHAPTER SIX

CLEANING HOUSE

It was for freedom that Christ set us free;
therefore keep standing firm and do not be subject
again to a yoke of slavery."
Galatians 5:1

I can remember when my mother had just baked some peanut butter cookies and I asked if I could have some. She told me that I needed to wait until I had supper. Being the hungry and determined child that I was, when she left the room I proceeded to be disobedient. I reached into the cookie jar and grabbed a handful, quickly retreating to my bedroom where I immediately ate them. Right when I was about to wipe the evidence from my face, my mother walked in and said, "Ronnie what did I say about the cookies?" I just smiled and said, "Mother, the devil made me do it!" Well, maybe it was the devil and maybe it wasn't. The bottom line is, we need to start taking responsibility for our actions and stop blaming everyone else for our failings.

Is taking care of your house an act of vanity? Of course not, unless you put it before God. Do you keep your house

81

clean and your yard picked up? Do you just throw your dishes in the cupboard or do you try to stack them in some organized fashion? Do you wash all your clothes together or on the same cycle or do you care enough to separate delicate from denim and reds from whites? If you need an oil change do you put in any oil or do you put in what's best for your vehicle? When you decide to paint a room do you grab any color and then throw the paint on the wall?

Well, some of us treat our true house, which is our body—God's temple, worse than we treat our pets, our cars or our boats. It is a wonder that our bodies withstand some of the abuse we heap upon it. We wouldn't think of running exhaust fumes into our house, yet some people are doing that when they smoke. You wouldn't build a three-story house on a foundation designed for one story, but some people have three to four times their normal weight bearing down on their bones. We must throw away every excuse for mistreating our body. We are going to have to change.

One of the first things you must do to grow spiritually is eliminate or toss out those things in your life that you know are not of God. Those are the things that will hinder you from being close to God. Then you need to pray and ask God to forgive you for allowing those things in your life and ask Him to help you in those areas. It is much the same in the physical sense. If you want to be in better health there are some things you will need to toss out. You might have to go through all your cupboards and look for items you know are high calorie or have high fat content and throw them out because those are the kind of foods that will lead you in the opposite direction of where you want to go.

When you are done purging your kitchen, restock your cupboards with foods that will benefit you. Much like when you stock up on spiritual books to nourish and strengthen your soul, it will be important that you stock up on foods that will nourish you physically. Choose foods such as fresh fruits and vegetables, fish, low-fat foods, and foods with lower sodium content. There are plenty of resources out there on nutrition that you can utilize as you build a healthy kitchen. But I encourage you to stay away from fad and hype. Try to keep it simple. A good rule of thumb is stick as close to the natural food source as possible. For example, instead of a banana muffin, eat a banana. Avoid processed foods. Again, keep it simple.

Please don't forget to throw out those oversized clothes...you know the ones that you keep in your closet just in case you gain the weight back. Well, my friend, if you keep those clothes in your closet you are like a double minded man unstable in all his ways because you don't know if you will lose that weight for good or gain it all back. If you want complete freedom and victory throw them all out or give them away. Then, if you can afford to buy some new clothes, do so in the size you desire to be. That will motivate and encourage you to stick to your plan. Do not forget 1 Corinthians 10:31 which states, "Therefore, whether you eat or drink or whatever you do, do all to the glory of God."

Am I saying you can never eat certain kinds of food again? Heavens no! What I am saying is that being around certain types of food, to some people, is like leaving a door open to sin. "Therefore, to one who knows the right thing to do and does not do it, to him it is sin" (James 4:17). If you know you have a problem with certain types of food you will have to do your part to stay clear of them and then pray that God would give you a desire to eat healthier foods. Ask God to give you wisdom and new insight into what you buy and eat. The bible clearly states that if anyone lacks wisdom let him ask God who gives it liberally (James 1:5). Pray for wisdom and believe God for it. If you really want help in that area of your life, God will help you to make wise decisions.

Is Overeating Really a Sin?

Overeating is the sin of gluttony. I know most people don't want to hear that because so much of their social and church lives surround food. How could something that brings people together be a sin? Sad to say, instead of fellowship and breaking bread we are more often participating in food orgies. We go through the food line of good old southern cooking and load up on fried chicken, macaroni and cheese, and sweet potato casserole complete with mini-marshmallows. Or maybe it's the church potluck with casseroles of every kind and dessert bars and cookies as far as the eye can see. We go back for refills as long as there is food to be eaten. Then we either sit back and rub our stomachs like we have just conquered some monumental task or we groan and unbutton our top button and think, "I shouldn't have eaten that."

What part of that scenario glorifies God? Is having fellowship and breaking bread together wrong? Absolutely not! What is sin is over-indulgence to the point of gluttony and to the harm of our body. For example, a fit and trim person can have dessert in moderation with neither gluttony nor harm to the body. Another person, who is over-weight and already putting a tax on the body, couldn't eat that dessert without it inflicting more harm to the body. It is especially sad when I see pastors standing before the congregation exhorting the people to repent from their sin and follow the ways of God in His grace, yet they have never done so for themselves in the area of gluttony. Overeating and not taking care of one's body is not a sin you can hide. It is right there in the forefront. Yet it is a sin many people tend to over-look and for which they easily make excuses. It has been labeled a 'will power' issue instead of a sin issue.

The Good News is...

With God's help you can over-come sin. With God's help you can overcome your habit of overeating. The bible clearly states that we reap what we sow. In other words, garbage in and garbage out. A lot of Christians are not sickly because of the devil but because of their own neglect and lack of concern for their health. If you truly believe God answers prayer, then pray for God's help and He will help you. Notice that I said *help* because He will not do the work for you but empower you to do what you know is right to do. If you can turn from sin you can turn from food. If you seek the kingdom of God first and foremost then all the other things you want according to His will shall be added onto you, but you have to believe for your victory to become a reality.

Nutritionally Speaking

I am going to tell you something that will simplify your eating and at the same time make it easy for you to follow. There are so many diets out there for losing weight and I am not going to recommend or even mention any of them. What I am going to recommend is what I call the 'common sense' diet. To be successful you need something you can follow your entire life and that, my friend, is Jesus. Yes, Jesus first and then moderation in everything else. Spiritual growth by means of prayer, worship, and the Word of God is the one area that you never get enough of in this life. When it comes to your eating and the amount of time you commit to exercise, you need to use good common sense along with moderation. For those of you that have a hard time disciplining yourself with eating and motivating yourself to exercise, start each day praying and believing in the name of Jesus. Ask for help in controlling what you put into your mouth as well as applying exercise for that day, then thank

85

Jesus for answering your prayer. Be encouraged! All things are possible if you only believe (Matthew 19:26).

Let's make one thing very clear: do not consume one high fat meal after another and expect Jesus to keep you lean and mean. On the flip side, don't eat like a bird and expect Jesus to miraculously develop huge muscles. Jesus could do that because He is God, but I do not believe God is going to perform a miracle in an area that just requires us to take action. If you want to lose weight and keep it off, you need to burn more calories than you take in. Plain and simple. Eat four to five small meals a day and drink a minimum of six to eight glasses of water a day. Time some of your water intake about one-half hour before each meal. Sometimes people think they're hungry when, in actuality, they are thirsty. Do some aerobic exercise along with some weight training. The more muscle you have the more calories you will burn, even if you are just sitting! It has been shown that exercise increases your metabolism hours after you are done.

If you want to gain weight, you need to take in more calories than you burn off and do more weight bearing exercises. Just make sure the majority of your calorie intake is from healthy foods. Your doctor or dietitian should be able to suggest an eating plan for healthy weight gain. Of course, for optimum fitness, aerobic activity is recommended along with the weight training.

When you feel like you want to slip back into your old eating habits, remember that what you put inside will not only effect what you see outside, but it will also effect what happens on the inside. A calorie is a calorie is a calorie, which basically means if you take in more calories than you burn off you will eventually gain some unwanted weight. In some respects our body is like a car. If we constantly carry more weight in our vehicle than what it was designed for it will wear out or run down the engine sooner or later. Like our cars, if we carry excess weight we will be putting more strain on our body, which will ultimately put our bodies in a precarious position. Strain on our heart, circulatory system, digestion, skeletal system...just about every physiological system we have is at risk for malfunction. But if we watch our weight and what we eat we will find our body running smoother and find ourselves needing less prayer in that area.

Let's be mature Christians and start dealing with the sin of neglecting our body and indulging in gluttony. Let's get out of the prayer line for physical ailments that could be remedied through better self-care and get in the exercise line at the health club. Let's hit the salad bar and stay away from the dessert bar. It's time to grow up and live a life that reflects the joy, health, power, and stamina of someone who has gained control over these areas. If you were making the devil mad in ministry before, just wait until you get in shape!

I remember visiting a number of friends of mine at Pillsbury Bible College in Owatonna, Minnesota. I used to wonder what they had that I didn't have because it seemed easier for them to walk with God and for me it was a constant struggle—one that I was losing. I wasn't struggling because God failed me but struggling because I failed myself. Looking back now it is easy to see why I failed. I had heard sermon after sermon about loving your Lord and Savior with all your heart, with all your soul, and with all your might (Deuteronomy 6:5), but all I ever gave the Lord was my crumbs. That's right, a little time in the Word every now and then and an occasional bible study. Yet, I was always at church when the doors were open. Except, of course, if I had a hot date and then I would try to put the Lord out of my mind as quickly as I could. Well, the bible clearly says you cannot serve two masters. You must love the one and hate the other because anything that replaces God as first in your life is bound to lead you in the wrong direction.

The bible also talks about how many people hear the Word of God but deny the power of it. In other words, they hear the Word of God but don't treat it like it is true and living and able to transform their lives. That was me! I gave God literally nothing and I felt that He gave me nothing back. If I would have put to practice what I had learned I would have had a full life in Christ.

How does this apply to you? Maybe you have an eating disorder or you lack the discipline to eat the way you know you should or you lack the motivation to exercise or a host of other problems. God wants you to prosper and be in good health. If you really want to change how you eat and what you do, pray to the Father which is in heaven and He will hear you and answer your prayers as long as it is according to His will. If all you do after reading this book is make excuses on why you can't lose weight or why you don't start exercising, then you will be like I was. I was hearing the truth but not accepting or acting on that which I knew was right. One thing you need to remember is that this journey requires faith—not medical science. You do not know what a force you will be for the kingdom of God until you get your body in the kind of shape God wants you to be in.

Declarations

The bible is full of the promises of God toward us. It does our heart, soul, and mind good to remind ourselves of His goodness. Take some time to read aloud the following declarations, then recite them at times when you are struggling.

- o I declare in the name of Jesus that I am more than a conquer.

- In the name of Jesus I will not be controlled by what I see but by what I know.
- In the name of Jesus I rebuke anything that controls me.
- In the name of Jesus I declare God is my source.
- I command restraint in the name of Jesus.

In the name of Jesus I ask for help with self-control.

Thank You, Lord, for answering all my prayers, Amen.

Letting Go of the Old Man

Always remember, if you're a Christian you are a new man. 2 Corinthians 5:17 states, "Therefore if any man be in Christ, he is a new creature: old things are passed away; behold, all things are become new." The old man couldn't lose the excess weight but the new man can. The new man can start controlling his appetite if he truly wants to. I once heard a preacher say that there is a pound of pain in discipline and a ton of pain in regret. In other words, how will you feel years later when you realize that the state of your physical condition could have been controlled if you would have just acted upon what you knew was right to do. You will not be able to claim your innocence because there is so much information on health and nutrition out there...and you are reading this book! Put those old thoughts of defeat and all those magical diet claims in the closet. They didn't work in the past and they are not going to work now. The apostle Paul says it right in Philippians 3:13: "...but one thing I do: forgetting what lies behind and reaching forward to what lies ahead."

Personal Help

If you want to succeed in this or any other exercise program then you will need a personal trainer, and if you're going to hire one, hire the best. Hire someone who has impeccable references. Many trainers claim expertise but do not have a good track record. Find someone who will care about and focus on *you* during the session. A good trainer will be well worth the cost.

Most importantly, I want you to call on Jesus, the Author and Finisher of our faith, and ask Him to guide you. The great news is that He will! Then listen to his voice when He speaks. It is important, as you are learning to walk with God in this realm, to not feel defeated or hopeless when you miss it. Don't be surprised if you are less than perfect on occasion. I have missed it physically and spiritually at times and I refuse to come under condemnation, and neither should you. God does not condemn. He convicts and the Holy Spirit draws us closer to Him.

As a trainer, people expect me to be 'up' and an energetic motivator. As a child of God, those that know me also expect me to deal with the stresses of life a little differently. Staying in shape helps to alleviate and diminish those stresses that might have hurt my body. Praying helps to soothe and heal the troublesome or worrisome mind. That is why it is important to have balance in mind, body, and spirit. Seek first the kingdom of God and HIS RIGHTEOUSNESS and all these other things—whether physical or financial—will come in His perfect timing if it is according to God's will. Let's not forget 2 Peter 3:8-9 (NIV): "But do not forget this one thing, dear friends: With the Lord a day is like a thousand years, and a thousand years are like a day," and Numbers 23:19 (NIV), "God is not human, that he should lie, not a human being, that he should change his mind. Does he speak and then not act? Does he promise and not fulfill?" Don't get discouraged if what you are seeking does not come as quickly as you want. God is faithful and will provide in His time.

Set Your Boundaries

Having and setting boundaries is important to anything we do in life, but for the purpose of this book, I am more concerned with the boundaries you allow to be set for yourself unknowingly, whether spiritually or physically. We must at all times remain in control of our lives. Too often, as married couples, when one spouse decides to stop going to church it isn't long before the other one decides to stop going. Perhaps it is a friend or group of friends that stops going to church and you are tempted to follow suit. My friend, it is important for you to have an individual relationship with Jesus so that you are not influenced negatively by other people's lack and concern for their relationship with the Lord. You know the saying, "misery loves company." Well, this is true even with Christians who backslide. When you're falling off a cliff the natural thing to do is reach out for something or someone to grab onto. You are not too concerned with the fact that you might be pulling them down as a Christian when you backslide. We have a tendency to pull important people in our lives in the direction we are heading, because if we leave them in a state where they are living righteously, it will only make us feel more convicted in our sin.

That is why it is important to make sure that whomever you choose to marry loves God more than they love you. You want someone who will always encourage you and someone you know is sold out to Jesus completely. The type of spouse I am talking about is one who, if they feel themselves slipping, will not stop going to church but will persevere until they get set free from whatever it is that is attacking their spirit. No matter what we say, once you know the truth, the truth will indeed make you free if we act upon it.

Taking care of your body is no different. Let's say you get

married and you and your spouse make an agreement to work out three days a week. One of you starts missing workouts. You as an individual have to stick with what you know is the right thing to do and you cannot let your spouse's attitude on working out affect yours. The truth is, when you exercise you do feel better, you have more energy, and the likelihood of increasing your longevity is greatly enhanced. Remember, I said the truth will make you free. That is directly from the bible and the truth will make you free in all areas of your life if you act upon it.

If you are physically arrested and are placed behind bars, the judge may say, "You are now free". You may be technically free, but you are not physically free until you walk out of that jail cell. The same is true with our body. We will not be free until we get up off the couch, put the chips down, and start taking advantage of the freedom God has ordained us to have physically.

Do you see the correlation? So many people of faith are spiritually free, for they walk in the light of his Word. However, they are physically in the dark because they do not take the physical action that is needed to be where God would have them. I pray that the light of Jesus will shine on all areas of your life and that you will take whatever steps are necessary to be free.

Grieving the Spirit

Let me give it to you plain and simple: if you're a born-again Christian who is living for God and you are over-weight or out of shape then the Holy Spirit has probably spoken to you. You know that voice in your head that says you need to eat less and start working out. Instead of taking it seriously, you laugh it off like so many people do and tell yourself you will cut back on eating after the holiday season, only to find another holiday right around the corner. You have probably sat through even a sermon or two and heard a pastor talk briefly about the fact that we need to take better care of ourselves. Now, you notice, I said you probably heard a sermon or two. That's because this subject is so seldom mentioned in church. I believe it is because most pastors worry that they might offend some of their members if they brought up the weight or health issue, when, in fact, if this message was brought up properly, most members would probably thank their pastors and stop grieving the Spirit.

Grieving the Spirit by Overeating

How many times have you continued eating even though you know you should have stopped? When we sit at the kitchen table and constantly overeat we really have no one to blame but ourselves. We can say the devil made us do it, but it really was our lack of discipline that caused us to grab that extra piece of pie. When I was young, I remember watching a comedian on TV named Flip Wilson. One of his lines was "the devil made me do it!" At the time we used to think that was so funny. Looking back and knowing what I know now, it really wasn't funny at all because it kept us from really looking at the problem. That problem was ourselves and not the devil. We heard that repeated so many times that whenever we got caught doing something wrong we would say "the devil made us do it."

Grieving the Spirit through Negativity

When negative attitudes are projected or spoken by you, the Holy Spirit is grieved and you will inevitably receive negative results. Remember, it causes you more pain to do a negative act than it does to do a positive act. I have never seen anyone go far in business, sports, or any other field that had a negative attitude. Negative talk can delay you from reaching

93

your physical or mental destiny. A quote from Proverbs 16:24 says, "Pleasant words are a honeycomb, sweet to the soul and healing to the bones." If the people around you aren't supportive of your efforts then stay away from them. I believe it to be truly universal and spiritual that what you put into life you will get back. By you being positive and surrounding yourself with positive people, you are increasing or quickening your chances of success.

Excuses vs Truth

We have all used excuses from time to time to escape the full consequence of our actions. We may even come to believe them ourselves. Some people never take responsibility for their decisions and behaviors in life, which leads to dysfunction in their everyday lives and relationships. Maybe you have used some of the following:

- o I barely have time for church.
- o I barely have time to pray.
- o I don't have the time to read my bible, let alone exercise.
- o My kids take up all my time.
- o Working out is vain.
- o I have always been fat, so what's' the use?
- o I don't like to sweat.
- o I am embarrassed to show my full figure.
- o If there were only more hours in the day.

Well, my friend, there aren't more hours in a day. Of all the things we need to do in our busy lives, our primary responsibility should be to the things of God. The bible clearly says to seek the kingdom of God first and foremost, then all these other things we need will be provided to us.

Everything in life takes time. That's why it's so important

that we manage our time wisely. In fact, writing this book took me many hours, but I believed there was such a need for a book that dealt with the subject of balancing faith and fitness that I made time where there was none. If we're living the kind of life God wants us to live and commands us to live, we can have complete peace in our hearts. Our soul and spirit live in a physical body and as long as we are living in this physical body we will be governed by the laws of the body. No matter how much peace you have in your heart, it won't make your body healthier. So, let's set aside the excuses and look at some evidence of fitness and faith:

- o Slows down the aging process
- o Increase in energy
- o Lowers blood pressure
- o Increased metabolism
- o Feel better
- o Look better
- o Sleep better
- o Decrease in susceptibility to disease
- o Increased sense of well-being

Shall I go on? I could write page after page of benefits from physical and spiritual health.

Only you can decide your fate. You can choose right now to live a rich and full spiritual and physical life. The choice is yours and always will be. As I said earlier, if you want to have total peace in your heart you will have to give it all to Jesus. If you want the verdict to be good health then you will have to give it all to Jesus, too. Yes…it will take physical work to obtain a healthy body. Talk to the Holy Spirit right now and ask for guidance and strength. Then, when he tells you to do something, do it. Don't just stand there. When the Holy Spirit speaks and you don't listen, He is grieved. How would you feel if you gave one of your kids great advice and they didn't listen? I believe the Holy Spirit feels the same way. You can choose life or choose death. The choice is yours.

Track and Feel

When you first see these words, *track and feel,* you may think it is a typo for *track and field.* You might think of sprinters, long distance runners, pole vaulting, shot put, long jump, and more. What I am talking about has nothing to do with sports but everything to do with accountability. In this section, I am asking that you first, record your physical activities for the day. Secondly, I am asking that you record how you feel after each day that you work out. Finally, I would ask you to record what you are doing daily to build yourself spiritually. Try doing this for at least 21 days and see if it helps you become more energized and focused on the things of God. Why do I want you to keep records? Because I have found over the years that those who kept records were more likely to stick to an exercise program. Their record book was right in their face, reminding them of their contract and commitment.

Stay on Guard

Research shows that a sharp mind is easier to maintain when you are physically fit. When you are out of shape it is easier for us to let those foxes spoil the vine. If the body is tired the mind is certain to follow. In a study reported by the Journal of Sports Medicine and Physical Fitness in 2001, 80 young male and female volunteers were tested for mood and then did aerobics for an hour. Of the 80, 52 were depressed before the exercise. That group was the most likely to benefit, reporting a reduction in anger, fatigue, and tension. They also felt more vigorous after the workout.

There can be many forms of 'foxes' out there that could

spoil your vine and we are told to be on guard, to be sober, and to be vigilant because our adversary walks about as a roaring lion seeking whom he may devour (1 Peter 5:8). Growing up, I remember people frequently said, "An idle mind is the devil's workshop." Well, perhaps they were not too far off. Many of our struggles start in our minds. Let's protect what we have by staying on guard because the spirit is willing, but the flesh is weak; in all these things we can be more than conquerors.

TIME FOR ACTION

It is self-defeating to start moving toward a healthier lifestyle and yet have cookies, ice cream, donuts, and chips in your house. It is as tempting as someone who struggles with addiction having alcohol in the cupboard. Don't tempt yourself! Set yourself up for success, not failure. Take stock of your life and see what other areas you are tempting yourself or setting yourself up for failure and do what you need to do to set yourself up for success. Success in one area will inevitably lead to success in another.

Is Overeating Really a Sin?

1. Do you eat when you aren't hungry? Explain:

_____

_____

_____

_____

_____

_____

_____

_____

2. Do you continue to eat after you are no longer hungry?
   Explain:

   _____
   _____
   _____
   _____
   _____
   _____

3. Over the next 3 days, try eating only when you are
   experiencing hunger. You may have forgotten what
   hunger feels like. Wait for about ten minutes after you
   feel the hunger pang and see if it passes.

Write down your experiences:

Day 1:

   _____
   _____
   _____
   _____
   _____
   _____
   _____
   _____

Day 2:

   _____
   _____
   _____
   _____
   _____
   _____
   _____

Day 3:

_____
_____
_____
_____
_____
_____
_____
_____

The Good News is...

The Holy Spirit can help you overcome the sin of gluttony. Be honest. Be humble. Ask the Lord forgiveness and the power to overcome temptation. Like the bondage of any sin, God can forgive and empower anyone to do what is right. If you need to, take time right now and invite the Lord into this struggle with food and see Him move powerfully in this area of your life.

Declare God's goodness and power over your life. Add additional declarations that are specific to you and your situation. Most importantly, practice these declarations on a daily basis:

I declare in the name of Jesus that I am more than a conqueror.

In the name of Jesus, I will not be controlled by what I see but by what I know.

In the name of Jesus, I rebuke anything that controls me.

In the name of Jesus, I declare God is my source.

I command restraint in the name of Jesus.

I will ask the Lord for help with self-control.

I declare:

_____
_____
_____
_____
_____
_____
_____
_____
_____
_____

I will:

_____
_____
_____
_____
_____
_____
_____
_____
_____
_____

Thank you, Lord, for answering all my prayers. In Jesus name, Amen.

Set Your Boundaries

Boundaries are like fences. You put a fence up to keep kids and pets in, to define your property, and to keep unwanted animals and people out. Apply this to your health and fitness.

1. What good habits and activities do you want to keep?

_____

_____

_____

_____

_____

_____

2. Draft a statement that defines your mission for health and fitness:

_____

_____

_____

_____

_____

_____

3. What influences that you want to keep out of your life have been a particular challenge for you?

_____

_____

_____

_____

_____

_____

Track and Feel

Record your physical activities for each day. Next, write down how you feel after each day that you exercised. Finally, record what you have done each day to build yourself up spiritually. Do this exercise for 21 days and write down a final summation of your experience. Keep this to encourage yourself both physically and spiritually. It's a good exercise to use as a refresher throughout your health-quest journey. Complete the following chart:

	Physical Exercise	How I feel	Spiritual Exercise
Day 1			
Day 2			
Day 3			
Day 4			
	Physical Exercise	How I Feel	Spiritual Exercise
Day 5			
Day 6			
Day 7			
Day 8			
Day 9			
Day 10			

Day 11			
Day 12			
Day 13			
Day 14			
Day 15			
Day 16			
Day 17			
Day 18			
Day 19			
Day 20			
Day 21			

1. Summarize how you felt after the 21-Day exercise above:

_____

_____

_____

_____

_____

_____

_____

_____

_____

_____

_____

_____

_____

_____

_____

POWER VERSES

It was for freedom that Christ set us free; therefore keep standing firm and do not be subject again to a yoke of slavery. Galatians 5:1

Whether, then, you eat or drink or whatever you do, do all to the glory of God. 1 Corinthians 10:31

Therefore, to one who knows the right thing to do and does not do it, to him it is sin. James 4:17

But if any of you lacks wisdom, let him ask of God, who gives to all generously and without reproach, and it will be given to him. James 1:5

And looking at them Jesus said to them, "With people

this is impossible, but with God all things are possible.
Matthew 19:26

Therefore if anyone is in Christ, he is a new creature; the
old things passed away; behold, new things have come.
2 Corinthians 5:17

Brethren, I do not regard myself as having laid hold of it
yet; but one thing I do: forgetting what lies behind and
reaching forward to what lies ahead, Philippians 3:13

But do not let this one fact escape your notice, beloved,
that with the Lord one day is like a thousand years,
and a thousand years like one day. The Lord is not slow
about His promise, as some count slowness, but is patient
toward you, not wishing for any to perish but for
all to come to repentance. 2 Peter 3:8-9

Pleasant words are a honeycomb, sweet to the soul and
healing to the bones. Proverbs 16:24

CHAPTER SEVEN

PRAY IT FORWARD

And as it is appointed unto men once to die,
but after this the judgment:
Hebrews 9:27

Fitness and faith are not just for the present moment. It is much bigger and more meaningful than one would imagine. Fitness and faith affect generations beyond yourself. It is amazing how much impact you have on your children and grandchildren. I would venture to say your sphere of influence is quite large. You are an unwitting missionary of faith and health. Since we have such an influence, let's 'pray it forward' that God would help us to be the best missionaries we can be.

Redeeming the Time

Ephesians 5:15-17 states, "See then that ye walk circumspectly, not as fools, but as wise, redeeming the time, because the days are evil. Wherefore be ye not unwise but understanding what the will of the Lord is." The word "redeeming" in the Greek can mean "to buy up, ransom, or rescue from loss." We alone are responsible for using the time God has given to each of us to prepare for the calling that He has placed on our lives, whether in ministry or in the workplace. That is why it is important that we become great at managing our time.

I often talk about how much time we all would free up if we took out all of the magazines we have in our bathroom because those magazines can steal an extra 10 to 20 minutes per visit. If you looked at other things you do at home you'll find plenty of other time stealers. If you take smoke breaks at work, social media peeks that add up to an hour before you know it, checking emails frequently, or playing electronic games on your computers or cell phones, these can steal away more time than we think. Satan will use anything to distract us from what God has for us to do while we are here on this earth. We can only redeem today and plan to redeem tomorrow for yesterday is gone.

Pray it Forward Parents

As parents, we have to realize that everything we do or say will have tremendous effects on our kids. At the local shopping mall, I have often seen parents walking by me with their kids and, nine times out of ten, if the parent is overweight, then the children are usually overweight. When I see children who are proportionate to their size they usually have parents who are more weight and height appropriate. What does this all mean? It means that from the time your child can see and walk they are recording your actions. Like any child, they love to mimic their parents. So they eat what you eat and do what you do. If you sit at the TV set all day they will want to do that, too. That is why it is so important that, whether we feel like exercising or not, we must do it for ourselves and our children. If our kids grow up in an environment where they see their parents working out and respecting their bodies they will more likely workout. We want the best for our children. Let's start by showing them how to live.

My Father's Story

I remember one day when my father was visiting me at my workout studio in Minneapolis, I jokingly said, "Father, get up on those two bars and see how long you can hold your legs straight out in front of you." My father looked at me and said, "Why? Is that supposed to be hard?" I told him I just wanted to see if he could do it. My father positioned himself on the two bars and proceeded to raise his legs straight out into a perfect L position. He held that position for almost an entire minute. It was amazing to watch because most people under the age of 30 would be doing well if they could hold their legs up for half that time. I am fortunate to have parents who believe in exercise. My father works out with weights two to three times a week and rides a stationary bike at least three days a week. He is still able to do pull-ups and multiple reps of various exercises...and he is in his 90s!

My father is a good example of how exercise can enhance your physical life. If you saw my father walking you would think he's on a mission because he walks so fast. He moves like someone much younger. Although he stopped working years ago, he did not stop working out. I have always hated the word *retire*. When I look at that word I think it tends to mean shut down or quit. I prefer the word r*efire*—to ignite, to inspire, to renew! If you have completed your assignment and prepared yourself physically for the later years of life you will feel like a rocket ship ready to explore new territories and new horizons. You will have the energy to do it. My desire for you is that you not only take this journey but that you would encourage your children to follow by your example. You can live a long and full life if you stay on a consistent exercise program and healthy eating plan. My desire for you is that you not only recognize these truths but that you act upon them while you can.

As a Christian, my father has always been involved with church by being treasurer, singing in the choir, and being involved with several bible studies. Although he is retired, he volunteered one day a week at one of the inner-city schools. I believe if my father was not in good shape he would not have the energy or stamina to do the things he does. If you're a Christian and you're living for God but you just don't have any energy, let this be an encouragement to you. It does not matter how old you are. You can improve the quality of your physical life the same way you improve the quality of your spiritual life.

Heredity is Overrated

I believe that heredity is overrated when it comes to our spiritual health. I'm not saying that people can't be covered in prayer if they have a praying parent because they can be. But ultimately, each of us are responsible for ourselves. The writer of Hebrews states, "And without faith it is impossible to please Him, for he who comes to God must believe that He is and that He is a rewarder of those who seek Him" (11:6). When it comes to our physical health it is no different. We need to believe that God wants and desires us to walk in good health because a body that is not exercised will atrophy at a quicker rate, and a mind that is not challenged and mentally stretched will lose ability to process, calculate, and remember at a much quicker rate.

Don't Be Quick to Judge

As Christians, when we see people that are overweight,

anorexic, or just plain out of shape, we should be the last person to think or say something negative. At times our comments or thoughts carry us down that negative path all the while knowing in our hearts that this behavior is wrong. For instance, when we see an obese person in a buffet line and the first thing we think is they shouldn't be at a buffet house, we assume that they don't care about their health. In most instances, they do care, but they can't get motivated enough to do something about it. In the same way that some Christians constantly backslide, many people go from this diet plan to that diet plan. They want to do right but just keep going back to their old ways. If you know someone that's struggling with weight problems, start praying that God would convict them in those areas and that their eyes would be open to all that God would have for them.

If you are struggling in the physical areas of your life you will have to go to war. You will have to seek God through prayer because if you have tried time after time to make physical changes in your body only to have failed, then you need Jesus Christ to intervene on your behalf. Your spirit might be willing, but your flesh might indeed be weak. Be patient in your quest to obtain physical health. Don't rush in to it. Take things slow and you will reach your goals in due time if you stay consistent with your training. Philippians 4:6 reads, "Be anxious for nothing, but in everything by prayer and supplication with thanksgiving let your requests be made known to God."

If you are always talking about Jesus but outwardly your physical actions do not match your spoken word, then the bible says you are a hypocrite. People will know you from what kind of fruit you bear. It is the same with your body. Remember, Jesus was a carpenter. He had to be in great shape because in those days they had to make every tool by hand and most of the hauling was done on their backs. They

111

did not have big cranes to lift and place their heavy loads, so it would be logical to believe that a carpenter would need to have the physique to do the job. If you have ever looked around any construction site, you probably noticed that the men and woman both seem to be in decent, if not great, shape. It's easy to see why, when you're lifting and hauling wood, metal, bricks, etc. It's like their job is one big workout. So what should you do? The obvious, of course, is to start some form of exercise but not for the outward results one might expect to obtain from a fitness-based regime. Do it for the many health benefits that fitness can provide. Once you begin a regular exercise program you will not only begin to feel better, but you will begin to look better.

Several years ago I saw a movie called *Miracle.* There was one scene in this movie that showed how excited the Americans were after winning the gold medal at the Olympics because they were the underdogs and no one ever believed they had a chance at winning. They disciplined themselves and won. I began to reflect upon what Jesus did for us on the cross and how He gave his life for mine. I was inwardly cheering and thanking Jesus for what He did. The road to good physical independence won't be easy, but if you commit and discipline yourself you will win in the end.

I hope that you realize that no matter what it is in life, if you need help, then go to Jesus who will give you whatever you need, as long as it is according to His will. Maybe it's a new job, maybe it is controlling your temper, maybe its patience. The key is faith. Faith in Jesus is the answer. He can heal, quiet the storm, save your soul, and move mountains. Many Christians have faith for everything else except discipline. We need to know that Jesus can be involved in all areas of our lives if we allow Him.

112

Reclaim Your Health for Christ

Several years ago, I was invited to be one of the speakers at the International Healing Conference at Redeeming Love Church in Minnesota. I respectfully accepted the opportunity to share what God had placed on my heart. Four weeks later I was preaching a Holy Ghost led message of *Reclaiming Your Health for Christ God's Way* to a standing room only crowd. I held nothing back in my message knowing people don't need someone who placates them, but they need a preacher who will preach the truth. The truth is, if we don't protect and respect what the Lord has given us we will lose it.

If we truly want life more abundantly then we need to stay healthy physically as well as spiritually. The message was direct and to the point, letting attendees know that God is not condemning their lack of obedience in these areas but He does *convict*. At the end of my message an altar call was given for prayer. Many came forward affirming that, when the truth is preached, conviction will come. After I had prayed for numerous people, a man approached me and asked me if I knew how old he was. I guessed he was around 65 years of age. He proudly put his hands on his hips, smiled and said, "I'm 80 years old!" Now that is what I am talking about when I stress a lifestyle of healthy eating and activity. That older gentleman was a man who loved God but also took care of his temple, which houses the Holy Spirit.

Or do you not know that your body is a temple of the Holy Spirit who is in you, whom you have from God, and that you are not your own?
1 Corinthians 6:19

What is Your Health Worth?

The first thing to do when starting a health and fitness

program is to take inventory of your habits, whether good or bad, and things about your body and lifestyle you would like to change. Use the self-analysis form below as a tool to help you take stock of your strengths and weaknesses. Review the information along the way to help you stay on track and encourage you as you progress toward health and fitness.

SELF-ANALYSIS FORM

Do you smoke? _____

Do you drink? _____

    More than once a week? _____

Are you overweight? _____

Are you under weight? _____

Do you have more fat on your body than muscle? _____

Do you have high cholesterol? _____

Do you have a high stress job? _____

Do you have high blood pressure? _____

Do you have back or knee pain? _____

Can you run 1/2 mile? _____

Can you do 20 push-ups? _____

Can you do 20 sit-ups? _____

Can you do 10 pull-ups (men)? _____

Can you bend over with your legs slightly bent and touch your toes? _____

Making it Happen

Keeping a positive attitude while you are changing your lifestyle for the better is important to the success of your venture. Combat every excuse for not following through with your health plan with a better reason for staying the course. Have some positive self-talk ready for moments of discouragement. I have used many bible verses in this book that are helpful to memorize and recite daily. There is power in the Word! Play the positive over and over again in your mind and let it saturate your heart and soul.

This book is titled *Balancing the Scales: Your Fitness Plan for Life*. It is not just about being fit and healthy physically but spiritually as well. Without spiritual fitness our physical fitness is meaningless. Take the following assessment and be honest with your answers.

For He knows the secrets of the heart.
Psalm 44:21

Recognizing the Truth

In this section write your thoughts down and be honest with yourself, for you and the Lord are the only ones that will see what you have written.

Have you accepted the Jesus Christ as your Savior? _____

Are you living for the Lord or have you fallen away from faith in Jesus Christ and the Christian walk?

_____
_____
_____
_____
_____

If you have fallen away, what has caused you to backslide?

_____

_____

_____

_____

_____

What is keeping you from accepting the Lord Jesus Christ as your Savior or getting your heart right with Jesus right now?

_____

_____

_____

_____

_____

No matter how healthy you become, if you are not born again you will not see the Kingdom of God.

TIME FOR ACTION

What you do today will not only affect *you* in the future but also your family and friends. You can be a positive influence to everyone around you. Just think of the power you have! Use it wisely and impact the future of generations to come.

Redeeming the Time

When it comes to exercise it is hard in our busy lives to find the time, yet things that waste our time are all around us and lure us into frittering away minute after minute. Answer the following questions regarding your time wasters:

1. Can you name some time wasters that steal minutes from you each day at home?

_____

_____

_____

At work?

_____

_____

_____

_____

_____

2. How much time would you save if you eliminated the above time wasters?

_____

_____

_____

_____

_____

3. What benefits would you enjoy without time wasters at home:

_____

_____

_____

_____

_____

At work:

_____

_____

_____

_____

_____

Make the most out of those saved minutes and invest in your physical and spiritual health. Chart your saved minutes for one week and see how much time you have for more important things.

	Time Waster Eliminated	What I Did Instead
Day 1		
Day 2		
Day 3		
Day 4		
Day 5		
Day 6		
Day 7		

4. Summarize how you felt after one week of the Time Waster exercise:

_____

_____

_____

_____

_____

_____

_____

_____

_____

Heredity is Over-rated

It is common knowledge that heredity can play a role in our physical make-up, health benefits, and health challenges but we also have a responsibility to take care of our bodies. We can't blame being out of shape on our genes. Review your family health history, jot down attributes and risks, then see how many of those risks can be mitigated by being a healthy weight, eating healthfully, and exercising regularly. I trust you will find that most of those risk factors will be diminished with good health habits.

Family Health Attributes:

_____

_____

_____

_____

_____

_____

_____

Family Health Risks:

_____

_____

_____

_____

_____

_____

_____

_____

_____

POWER VERSES

...because this He did once for all when
He offered up Himself. Hebrews 7:27a

Therefore be careful how you walk, not as unwise men but
as wise, making the most of your time, because the days
are evil. So then do not be foolish, but understand what the
will of the Lord is. Ephesians 5:15-17

And without faith it is impossible to please Him, for he who
comes to God must believe that He is and that He is a
rewarder of those who seek Him. Hebrews 11:6

Would not God find this out? For he knows the secrets
of the heart. Psalm 44:21

Or do you not know that your body is a temple of the Holy
Spirit who is in you, whom you have from God,
and that you are not your own?
1 Corinthians 6:19

For He knows the secrets of the heart.
Psalm 44:21

CHAPTER EIGHT

7-MINUTE FIT PARTY

What is the 7-Minute Fit Party, you might ask? The 7-Minute Fit Party is the first step in getting people to start to move on a daily basis and quote scripture at the same time. I know most people like parties. This is the party that is dedicated solely to you and your physical and spiritual health.

Before starting this 7-Minute Fit Party or any exercise program it is suggested that you check with a doctor, and if you are thinking about making any sudden changes to your diet tell your doctor about it, just to make sure you are on the right track.

The 7-Minute Fit Party is designed for those that have not exercised in years or are over the age of 50. The concept for my 7-Minute Fit Party came from something my church started. After each service, the pastors would all be assembled out in the lobby at different tables to meet new people who were visiting the church or anyone that had not connected with the pastors or staff. They would meet for a few minutes with anyone that stopped by. This seemed to work so well for our church that I thought this would be a good thing for people new to fitness or over the age of fifty to do. As a seasoned fitness trainer, I always like to come up with things that are innovative and different, so I came up with the 7-Minute Fit Party with one's self. Participants will take it slow and easy while getting to understand their own body and where they are health wise, and at the same time, will learn how to strengthen their spirit man.

For the 7-Minute Fit Party, I have included 12 exercises from my *Fitness and Faith Power Card Training System*. Each exercise comes with instructions on how to perform each exercise and includes a bible verse for biblical reflection for the complete set of cards. Go to www.fitnessking.com to order. Using the 7-Minute Fit Party training system can be altered to suit the individual's fitness level. But for the general public we recommend using them as instructed.

Participants of the fit party can pick one exercise at random or systematically, and each hour they will perform the exercise for 30 seconds nonstop. After 30 seconds they then will quote the bible verse as many times as they can for 30 seconds.

Although no weight is required for these exercises, light weight can be added where applicable. Feel free to alter this workout in any way that you like, keeping in mind that it is never the quantity of the exercises but it is the quality. So make sure to follow all instructions to get the most out of each exercise.

Start slow with each exercise and make every effort to use good form. Don't sacrifice form for a repetition. Remember to breathe out when you're exerting force, and most of all, use good form and take your time. Whether you add a few pounds of weight or not, the most important thing is not the weight but your level of concentration. This is because when you concentrate, your body doesn't really know if you have five pounds or eight pounds. Concentrate on each exercise and meditate on each verse. Don't be in a hurry because you did not get to where you are overnight. And, you won't make the change overnight either. Congratulations on making the decision to do something that will not only enhance you physically but will empower you spiritually.

If you want to kick it up a notch the second month, do two Seven Minute Fit Parties each hour of the day for a total of seven hours. You would do two exercises for 30 seconds each and then read two verses for 30 seconds each for a total of two minutes, and then each month you could add another minute to each hour and so on.

But I discipline my body and bring it into subjection, lest, when_I have preached to others, I myself should become disqualified. 1 Corinthians 9:27

TIME FOR ACTION

Fitness is a lifestyle. You can begin incorporating exercise into your day by following the 7-Minute Fit Party you learned about in this study guide, or you can work out in a way that is convenient enough for you to be consistent. I said *convenient enough* because almost anything that is good is not necessarily convenient. You will have to make a commitment to eating in moderation and exercising consistently. Too often people will make promises to themselves to lose weight and become more active but, like those New Year's Resolutions, they do not follow through. In reality, they have broken their promise to themselves. If we are going to keep a promise to anyone it should be to ourselves! How can you stay true to your word if you so easily break promises to yourself? If you say you are going to do something, then to the best of your ability DO IT! It will help you to believe in yourself. You will grow in character. You will put more value in what you say.

The last mental exercise of this study guide is to write a covenant with yourself. Draft a letter to yourself or a contract of what you will commit to with regards to your health and fitness (or anything else for that matter!). Do not write down anything that you are unwilling to do. You want to be a person of integrity; a person keeps their word.

MY FITNESS COVENANT

_____
_____
_____
_____
_____
_____
_____
_____
_____
_____
_____
_____
_____
_____
_____
_____
_____
_____
_____

POWER VERSES

But I discipline my body, and make it my slave, so that, after I have preached to others, I myself will not be disqualified. 1 Corinthians 9:27

No temptation has overtaken you but such as is common to man; and God is faithful, who will not allow you to be tempted beyond what you are able, but with the temptation will provide the way of escape also, so that you will be able to endure it. 1 Corinthians 10:13

...'Not by might nor by power, but by My Spirit,' says the Lord of hosts. Zechariah 4:6

Set a guard, O Lord, over my mouth; keep watch over the door of my lips. Psalm 141:3

He sent His word and healed them, and delivered them from their destructions. Psalm 107:20

Therefore I say to you, all things for which you pray and ask, believe that you have received them, and they will be granted you. Mark 11:24

My son, do not forget my teaching, but let your heart keep my commandments: Proverbs 3:1

Let your moderation be known unto all men. The Lord is at hand. Philippians 4:5 (KJV)

My son, give attention to my words; incline your ear to my sayings. Do not let them depart from your sight; keep them in the midst of your heart. For they are life to those who find them and health to all their body. Proverbs 4:20-22

Do you not know that you are a temple of God and that the Spirit of God dwells in you?" 1 Corinthians 3:16

For the kingdom of God is not eating and drinking, but righteousness, and peace, and joy in the Holy Spirit. Romans 14:17

Then I heard the voice of the Lord, saying, "Whom shall I send, and who will go for Us? Then said I, "Here am I. Send me!" Isaiah 6:8

Pray, then, in this way: Our Father who is in heaven, Hallowed be Your name. Matthew 6:9

MARCHING OR RUNNING IN PLACE
Cardiovascular Exercise

March or run in place lightly with your feet barely coming off the ground, moving at a pace that's comfortable for you for 30 seconds. Then read the following verse as many times as you can for 30 seconds.

No temptation has overtaken you except such as is common to man; but God is faithful, who will not allow you to be tempted beyond what you are able, but with the temptation will also make the way to escape, that you may be able to bear it.

1 CORINTHIANS 10:13

JUMPING ROPE IN PLACE
Cardiovascular Exercise

Stand with feet about 8 inches apart, elbows at waist level and bent. Mimic the movement of jumping rope for 30 seconds. Keep your steps light and feet close to the ground. You may jump with both feet together or alternate. Read the following verse as many times as you can for 30 seconds.

Not by might nor by power, but by my spirit, says the Lord of host.

ZECHARIAH 4:6

LAT PULL-DOWNS
Back/
Latissimus Dorsi

Extend arms overhead. Pull arms down while squeezing back muscles as hard as you can. Repeat this movement for 30 seconds. Now read the following verse as many times as you can for 30 seconds.

Set a guard, O Lord, over my mouth; Keep watch over the door of my lips.

PSALM 141:3

129

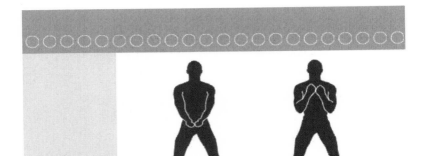

TWO ARM CURL
Biceps

Standing or sitting upright, palms should be facing and touching, held slightly below your waist. Curl both arms upward toward your chest and then back down. Repeat this movement for 30 seconds. Then read the following verse as many times as you can for 30 seconds.

He sent his word and healed them.

PSALM 107:20

130

SHOULDER PRESS
Trapezius,
Deltoids, Triceps
and Rhomboids

Standing or sitting upright, with hands slightly above your shoulders, with closed-fist facing forward, push both hands upwards without locking out the elbows, then lower hands. Repeat this movement for 30 seconds. Then read the following verse as many times as you can for 30 seconds.

Therefore I say to you, whatever things you ask when you pray, believe that you receive them, and you will have them.

MARK 11:24

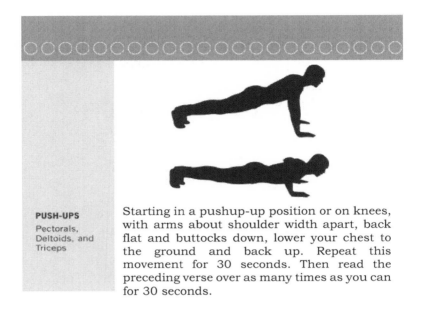

PUSH-UPS

Pectorals,
Deltoids, and
Triceps

Starting in a pushup-up position or on knees, with arms about shoulder width apart, back flat and buttocks down, lower your chest to the ground and back up. Repeat this movement for 30 seconds. Then read the preceding verse over as many times as you can for 30 seconds.

When you sit down to eat with a ruler, consider carefully what is before you.

PROVERBS 3:1

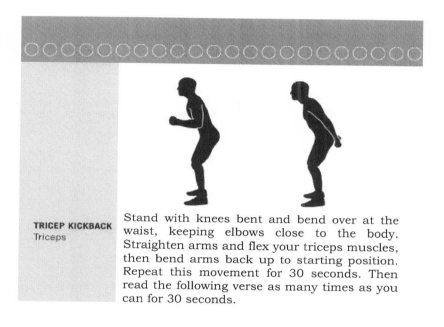

TRICEP KICKBACK
Triceps

Stand with knees bent and bend over at the waist, keeping elbows close to the body. Straighten arms and flex your triceps muscles, then bend arms back up to starting position. Repeat this movement for 30 seconds. Then read the following verse as many times as you can for 30 seconds.

Let your moderation be known unto all men. The Lord is at hand.

PHILIPPIANS 4:5

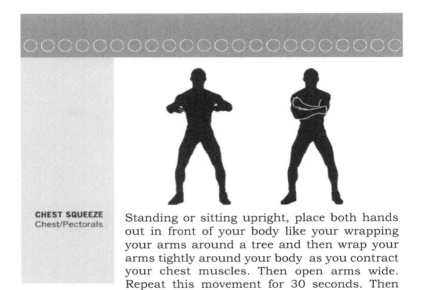

CHEST SQUEEZE
Chest/Pectorals

Standing or sitting upright, place both hands out in front of your body like your wrapping your arms around a tree and then wrap your arms tightly around your body as you contract your chest muscles. Then open arms wide. Repeat this movement for 30 seconds. Then read the following verse as many times as you can for 30 seconds.

My son, give attention to my words; Incline your ear to my sayings. Do not let them depart from your eyes; Keep them in the mist of your heart; For they are life to those that find them, And health to all their flesh.

PROVERBS 4:20-22

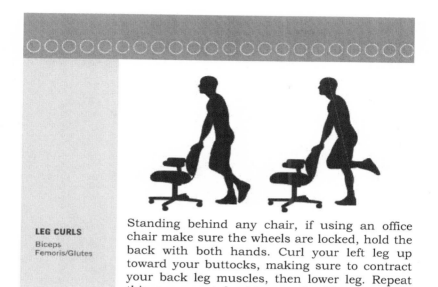

LEG CURLS

Biceps
Femoris/Glutes

Standing behind any chair, if using an office chair make sure the wheels are locked, hold the back with both hands. Curl your left leg up toward your buttocks, making sure to contract your back leg muscles, then lower leg. Repeat this movement for 30 seconds. Then read the following verse as many times as you can for 30 seconds. Repeat the above using your right leg.

Do you not know that you are the temple of God and that the spirit of God dwells in you?

1 CORINTHIANS 3:16

135

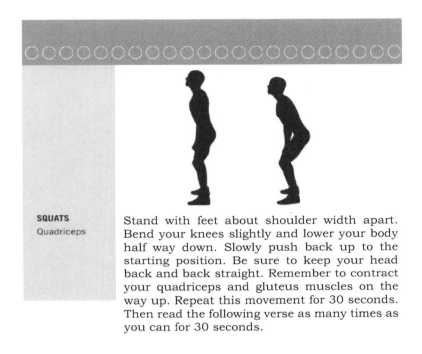

SQUATS
Quadriceps

Stand with feet about shoulder width apart. Bend your knees slightly and lower your body half way down. Slowly push back up to the starting position. Be sure to keep your head back and back straight. Remember to contract your quadriceps and gluteus muscles on the way up. Repeat this movement for 30 seconds. Then read the following verse as many times as you can for 30 seconds.

For the kingdom of God is not eating and drinking, but righteousness and peace and joy in the Holy Spirit.

ROMANS 14:17

Final Thoughts

I would not feel right closing this *Balancing the Scales* without encouraging you to share your gifts and what you have learned throughout this journey. Many people have fallen along the wayside, whether spiritually or physically. You could be the one that God is wanting to share the good news of freedom in Christ. We CAN have the victory over those areas that have had us bound.

Also I heard the voice of the Lord, saying, Whom shall I send, and who will go for us? Then said I, Here am I; send me."
Isaiah 6:8

I believe if we can submit ourselves fully to God, we too will say, "Here am I send me." And God will send us in spite of ourselves; in spite of our imperfect lives. Yet, He will be using people that have gone out of their way to be set apart and to be sanctified spiritually and physically through the blood of Jesus. We will truly be able to say,

Our Father in heaven, hallowed be your name. Your kingdom come, your will be done, on earth as it is in heaven.
Matthew 6:9

So pray it forward, my friend. Pray it forward.

ABOUT THE AUTHOR

Ron Henderson, "The Fitness King," began his pursuit of personal fitness training over three decades ago. Ron is the author of *Fitness Economics* and *Balancing the Scales: Your Fitness Plan for Life.* He was notably the first personal fitness trainer in the Minneapolis/St. Paul area to work with clients in their homes.

Ron's success and longevity in his field has made him an apt leader and innovator. His popularity as a media personality, corporate trainer, spokesperson, and speaker is nation-wide. Ron captivates and encourages audiences young and old alike, while educating, motivating, and inspiring them to enjoy more active lifestyles. He has trained top lawyers, CEOs, NFL players, and national recording stars and has helped them all to achieve physical fitness beyond what they could have done themselves.

Ron serves as a minister and leader in the Christian community. He is the host of the *Fitness and Faith* exercise series, the motivational series, *Motivation,* and former host of *The King and the Kids* workout show. He also co-hosted *Fan Fitness Sundays* on KFAN radio with local celebrity Mark Rosen. Ron has been featured regularly in newspapers and magazines for over three decades.

Ron Henderson "The Fitness King"

4301 Hwy 7 Suite 10
St. Louis Park, MN 55416

Visit www.fitnessking.com for more
information about Ron Henderson.

Contact Ron at ron@fitnessking.com

Made in the USA
Lexington, KY
12 November 2019

56885965R00095